The Sound Approach to birding

The Sound Approach to birding

A guide to understanding bird sound

MARK CONSTANTINE & THE SOUND APPROACH

Dedication
To Peter J Grant

Title: The Sound Approach to birding
Subtitle: A guide to understanding bird sound

Text: Mark Constantine & The Sound Approach

Sounds: Magnus Robb, Arnoud B van den Berg, Mark Constantine, Killian Mullarney & Dick Forsman
Sonagrams: Magnus Robb, Cecilia Bosman & Nick Hopper
Artwork: Killian Mullarney
Photographs: Arnoud B van den Berg, René Pop, Phil Koken, Killian Mullarney, Ruedi Aeschlimann, Mark Constantine, Kris De Rouck, Marten van Dijl, Dick Forsman, Roland Jansen & Magnus Robb

Sound editing and index: Magnus Robb
Photo editing and lithography: René Pop
Text editing: Arnoud B van den Berg & Magnus Robb
Graphic design: Birgit Schrama & Cecilia Bosman
Printed by Hoontetijl, Utrecht, Netherlands

Published by The Sound Approach, 29 High Street, Poole, Dorset BH12 1AB, UK © 2006

The Sound Approach: Arnoud B van den Berg, Mark Constantine & Magnus Robb

ISBN-10: 90-810933-1-2
ISBN-13: 978-90-810933-1-6
NUR-code: 435

Cover and labels: Firecrest and Goldcrest *(Killian Mullarney)*
Fly-leaf front: Gavarnie, Hautes-Pyrénées, France, September 1996 *(Arnoud B van den Berg)*
Fly-leaf back: Douz-Ghidma, Kebili, Tunisia, May 2005 *(René Pop)*

One way to order this book is to send £29.95 to: Lush, Times unit 3, 19 Willis Way, Fleets Industrial Estate, Poole, Dorset BH15 3SS, UK. You can also order by phone: +44(1)202-676622 or online www.lush.co.uk. Post and packing is free for the UK; for western Europe please add £3.00 for p&p and for the rest of the world £6.00.

Species guide to the accompanying CDs

See the main text for details such as location, date, age, sex, background species and catalogue number.

CD1-01a 0:00 – 0:15 **Grey Plover** *Pluvialis squatarola*
CD1-01b 0:17 – 0:31 **European Golden Plover** *Pluvialis apricaria*
CD1-01c 0:33 – 0:51 **American Golden Plover** *Pluvialis dominica*
CD1-01d 0:53 – 1:03 **Pacific Golden Plover** *Pluvialis fulva*
CD1-02a 0:00 – 0:20 **Great Bittern** *Botaurus stellaris*
CD1-02b 0:22 – 1:04 **Ural Owl** *Strix uralensis*
CD1-02c 1:06 – 1:25 **Common Cuckoo** *Cuculus canorus*
CD1-02d 1:27 – 2:00 **Little Owl** *Athene noctua*
CD1-02e 2:02 – 2:24 **Common Redshank** *Tringa totanus*
CD1-02f 2:26 – 2:48 **Common Sandpiper** *Actitis hypoleucos*
CD1-02g 2:49 – 3:22 **Goldcrest** *Regulus regulus*
CD1-02h 3:24 – 3:44 **Lesser Whitethroat** *Sylvia curruca*
CD1-03 **Common Grasshopper Warbler** *Locustella naevia*
CD1-04 **Savi's Warbler** *Locustella luscinioides*
CD1-05 **Common Ringed Plover** *Charadrius hiaticula*
CD1-06 **Little Ringed Plover** *Charadrius dubius*
CD1-07 **Red-throated Pipit** *Anthus cervinus*
CD1-08 **Mute Swan** *Cygnus olor*
CD1-09 **European Reed Warbler** *Acrocephalus scirpaceus*
CD1-10 **Sedge Warbler** *Acrocephalus schoenobaenus*
CD1-11 **Lanceolated Warbler** *Locustella lanceolata*
CD1-12 **River Warbler** *Locustella fluviatilis*
CD1-13 **Common Chiffchaff** *Phylloscopus collybita collybita*
CD1-14 **Willow Warbler** *Phylloscopus trochilus*
CD1-15 **Siberian Chiffchaff** *Phylloscopus collybita tristis*
CD1-16 **Iberian Chiffchaff** *Phylloscopus ibericus*
CD1-17 **Common Rosefinch** *Carpodacus erythrinus*
CD1-18 **Eurasian Curlew** *Numenius arquata*
CD1-19 **Stone-curlew** *Burhinus oedicnemus*
CD1-20 **Red Kite** *Milvus milvus*
CD1-21 **Black-eared Kite** *Milvus lineatus*
CD1-22 **Richard's Pipit** *Anthus richardi*
CD1-23 **Tawny Pipit** *Anthus campestris*
CD1-24 **Blyth's Pipit** *Anthus godlewskii*
CD1-25 **Mongolian Finch** *Bucanetes mongolicus*
CD1-26 **Trumpeter Finch** *Bucanetes githagineus*
CD1-27 **Yellow-browed Warbler** *Phylloscopus inornatus*

CD1-28 **Coal Tit** *Periparus ater*
CD1-29 **Pallas's Leaf Warbler** *Phylloscopus proregulus*
CD1-30 **Common Ringed Plover** *Charadrius hiaticula tundrae*
CD1-31 **Semipalmated Plover** *Charadrius semipalmatus*
CD1-32 **European Stonechat** *Saxicola rubicola*
CD1-33 **Siberian Stonechat** *Saxicola maurus*
CD1-34 **Red-breasted Flycatcher** *Ficedula parva*
CD1-35 **Winter Wren** *Troglodytes troglodytes*
CD1-36 **Taiga Flycatcher** *Ficedula albicilla*
CD1-37 **Herring Gull** *Larus argentatus*
CD1-38 **Caspian Gull** *Larus cachinnans*
CD1-39 **Yellow-legged Gull** *Larus michahellis*
CD1-40 **Lesser Black-backed Gull** *Larus fuscus*
CD1-41 **Great Spotted Woodpecker** *Dendrocopos major*
CD1-42 **Lesser Spotted Woodpecker** *Dendrocopos minor*
CD1-43 **Baillon's Crake** *Porzana pusilla*
CD1-44 **Thrush Nightingale** *Luscinia luscinia*
CD1-45 **Common Blackbird** *Turdus merula*
CD1-46 **Common Blackbird** *Turdus merula*
CD1-47 **Eurasian Woodcock** *Scolopax rusticola*
CD1-48 **Eurasian Woodcock** *Scolopax rusticola*
CD1-49 **Eurasian Magpie** *Pica pica*
CD1-50 **Great Northern Loon** *Gavia immer*
CD1-51 **Rock Ptarmigan** *Lagopus muta*
CD1-52 **Great Snipe** *Gallinago media*
CD1-53 **Common Snipe** *Gallinago gallinago* and **Great Snipe** *G media*
CD1-54a 0:00 – 1:25 **Three-toed Woodpecker** *Picoides tridactylus*
CD1-54b 1:27 – 2:20 **Three-toed Woodpecker** *Picoides tridactylus*
CD1-55 **Aquatic Warbler** *Acrocephalus paludicola*
CD1-56 **Caspian Snowcock** *Tetraogallus caspius*
CD1-57 **Caucasian Snowcock** *Tetraogallus caucasicus*
CD1-58 **Eurasian Skylark** *Alauda arvensis*
CD1-59 **Greater Hoopoe Lark** *Alaemon alaudipes*
CD1-60 **Horned Lark** *Eremophila alpestris*
CD1-61 **Wood Lark** *Lullula arborea*
CD1-62 **Brambling** *Fringilla montifringilla*
CD1-63 **Common Chaffinch** *Fringilla coelebs*
CD1-64 **European Greenfinch** *Chloris chloris*
CD1-65 **Short-billed Dowitcher** *Limnodromus griseus*
CD1-66 **Long-billed Dowitcher** *Limnodromus scolopaceus*

CD1-67	**Willow Tit** *Poecile montana*
CD1-68	**Marsh Tit** *Poecile palustris*
CD1-69	**Great Tit** *Parus major*
CD1-70	**European Blue Tit** *Cyanistes caeruleus*
CD1-71	**Common Tern** *Sterna hirundo*
CD1-72	**Arctic Tern** *Sterna paradisaea*
CD1-73	**Common Tern** *Sterna hirundo*
CD1-74	**Arctic Tern** *Sterna paradisaea*
CD1-75	**Common Tern** *Sterna hirundo*
CD1-76	**Arctic Tern** *Sterna paradisaea*
CD1-77	**Common Tern** *Sterna hirundo*
CD1-78	**Arctic Tern** *Sterna paradisaea*
CD1-79a	0:00 – 0:51 **Bohemian Waxwing** *Bombycilla garrulus*
CD1-79b	0:53 – 1:11 **Ring Ouzel** *Turdus torquatus*
CD1-79c	1:13 – 1:33 **European Robin** *Erithacus rubecula*
CD1-80a	0:00 – 0:41 **Common Chaffinch** *Fringilla coelebs*
CD1-80b	0:43 – 0:57 **Corn Bunting** *Emberiza calandra*
CD1-80c	0:59 – 1:09 **European Goldfinch** *Carduelis carduelis*
CD1-81	**Common Eider** *Somateria mollissima*
CD1-82	**Long-tailed Tit** *Aegithalos caudatus* and **'common crossbills'** *Loxia curvirostra*
CD1-83	**Water Rail** *Rallus aquaticus*
CD1-84	**Goldcrest** *Regulus regulus*
CD1-85	**Firecrest** *Regulus ignicapilla*
CD1-86	**Common Chiffchaff** *Phylloscopus collybita collybita*
CD1-87	**Common Chiffchaff** *Phylloscopus collybita collybita*
CD1-88a	0:00 – 0:18 **Mealy Redpoll** *Carduelis flammea*
CD1-88b	0:20 – 0:53 **Mealy Redpoll** *Carduelis flammea*
CD1-89	**Cetti's Warbler** *Cettia cetti*
CD1-90	**Cetti's Warbler** *Cettia cetti*
CD1-91	**Common Blackbird** *Turdus merula*
CD1-92	**Common Chaffinch** *Fringilla coelebs*
CD1-93	**Common Nightingale** *Luscinia megarhynchos*
CD1-94	**Common Nightingale** *Luscinia megarhynchos*
CD1-95	**Common Nightingale** *Luscinia megarhynchos*
CD1-96	**Blackcap** *Sylvia atricapilla*
CD1-97	**Blackcap** *Sylvia atricapilla*
CD1-98	**Blackcap** *Sylvia atricapilla*
CD1-99	**Garden Warbler** *Sylvia borin*

CD2-01	**Lesser Whitethroat** *Sylvia curruca*
CD2-02	**Lesser Whitethroat** *Sylvia curruca*
CD2-03	**Blyth's Reed Warbler** *Acrocephalus dumetorum*
CD2-04	**Marsh Warbler** *Acrocephalus palustris*
CD2-05	**Zitting Cisticola** *Cisticola juncidis*
CD2-06	**Savi's Warbler** *Locustella luscinioides*
CD2-07	**Common Grasshopper Warbler** *Locustella naevia*
CD2-08	**Common Grasshopper Warbler** *Locustella naevia*
CD2-09	**Yellow-browed Warbler** *Phylloscopus inornatus*
CD2-10	**Pallas's Leaf Warbler** *Phylloscopus proregulus*
CD2-11	**Siberian Chiffchaff** *Phylloscopus collybita tristis*
CD2-12	**Siberian Chiffchaff** *Phylloscopus collybita tristis*
CD2-13	**Marsh Warbler** *Acrocephalus palustris*
CD2-14	**European Reed Warbler** *Acrocephalus scirpaceus*
CD2-15	**Mistle Thrush** *Turdus viscivorus*
CD2-16	**Mistle Thrush** *Turdus viscivorus*
CD2-17a	0:00-0:22 **Mallard** *Anas platyrhynchos*
CD2-17b	0:23-0:51 **Mallard** *Anas platyrhynchos*
CD2-18	**Common Teal** *Anas crecca*
CD2-19	**King Eider** *Somateria spectabilis*
CD2-20	**Ruddy Duck** *Oxyura jamaicensis*
CD2-21	**Pectoral Sandpiper** *Calidris melanotos*
CD2-22a	0:00-0:05 **Pectoral Sandpiper** *Calidris melanotos*
CD2-22b	0:06-0:11 **Pectoral Sandpiper** *Calidris melanotos*
CD2-23	**Cory's Shearwater** *Calonectris borealis*
CD2-24	**Madeiran Storm-petrel** *Oceanodroma castro* cold-season type
CD2-25	**European Scops Owl** *Otus scops*
CD2-26	**Common Swift** *Apus apus*
CD2-27	**Pallid Swift** *Apus pallidus*
CD2-28	**Collared Flycatcher** *Ficedula albicollis*
CD2-29	**Western Orphean Warbler** *Sylvia hortensis*
CD2-30	**Desert Wheatear** *Oenanthe deserti*
CD2-31	**Common Blackbird** *Turdus merula*
CD2-32	**Great Reed Warbler** *Acrocephalus arundinaceus*
CD2-33	**Great Reed Warbler** *Acrocephalus arundinaceus*
CD2-34	**Blackcap** *Sylvia atricapilla*
CD2-35	**Common Starling** *Sturnus vulgaris*
CD2-36a	0:00-0:19 **Great Spotted Woodpecker** *Dendrocopos major*
CD2-36b	0:20-0:28 **Common Chaffinch** *Fringilla coelebs*
CD2-37	**Thrush Nightingale** *Luscinia luscinia*
CD2-38	**Marsh Warbler** *Acrocephalus palustris*
CD2-39	some species imitated during the first 20 seconds of the preceding track
CD2-40	**European Reed Warbler** *Acrocephalus scirpaceus*
CD2-41	**Blyth's Reed Warbler** *Acrocephalus dumetorum*

Contents

Acknowledgements

The Sound Approach are Arnoud B van den Berg, Mark Constantine and Magnus Robb. They would like to thank Per Alström, Graham Armstrong, Ewan Brodie, Martin Cade, Paul Duck, Pim Edelaar, Robert Gifford, George Green, Neil Hagger, Roger Howell, Jackie Hull, Nick Hull, Hannu 'Honey' Jannes, Lars Jonsson, Ian Lewis, James Lidster, Anthony McGeehan, Bruce Mactavish, Urban Olsson, John Raper, Shaun Robson, Steve Smith, Nigel Symes, Ian Wallace, Pim Wolf and Hugo Wood-Homer; Richard Ranft, the curator at the British Library of Wildlife Sounds, who took time to correct technical and biological aspects of the original paper; Paul Holt and Bill Jackson who shared their considerable knowledge of bird sounds and enthusiasm for recording; all at Cornell Lab of Ornithology, especially Greg Budney, the curator of the Macaulay Library (formerly Library of Natural Sounds), and WSB contenders 'The Sapsuckers', old and new; the editors of Birding World; the directors and customers of Limosa Holidays and Sunbird for their kindness, understanding and help; the wonderful Cecilia Bosman who, despite being put to the test by the team's behaviour, has kept an eye on everything from documenting the data through to the concept, design, and the details of the sonagrams; Killian Mullarney, who has been a true friend, made great recordings of mega rare birds, argued and illustrated the theories, refereed disputes, and corrected the grammar; Dick Forsman who, despite losing his car to Mark in a rash bet, helped find and record many birds; René Pop who, when not snoring, was an unsung hero; Mo Constantine and Ilse Schrama for calming heated situations and everlasting support; Birgit Schrama who stepped in at the last moment and helped with the organisation, the layout and design and saw the book through to the printers; family Constantine and family Haas for moral and technical support; and Nick Hopper for help with sonagram production and giving a birders' perspective. Thanks are also due for the support by many other persons and it is impossible to mention all of them. They include Hichem Azafzaf, Craig Benkman, Daniel Bergmann, Jacek Betleja, David Bigas, Marek Borkowski, Han Buckx, Richard Crossley, Giorgi Darchiasvili, Andrei Gavrilov, Ramaz Gokhelashvili, Gunnar Thor Hallgrimsson, Bernd Heinrich, Mark Herremans, Timur Iskakov, Yann Kolbeinsson, Andrej Koshin, Diana Krautter, Antero Lindholm, Erik Maassen, Eduardo Mínguez, Colm Moore, Manela Nunes, Daniele Occhiato, Ernesto Occhiato, Gerald Oreel, Pekka Pouttu, Vladimir Pozdnyakov, George Sangster, Roy Slaterus, Yuri Sofronov, Klas Strandberg, Ron Summers, António Teixeira, Thor Veen and Dick Woets.

Preface

Peter Grant and Killian Mullarney took bird identification to a new level with their seminal pamphlet *The new approach to identification*, first seen as a series of papers in Birding World, and then published privately in 1989. In it, they explained and summarised a terminology for plumage and age, moult, topography and other matters now considered fundamental in bird identification. Inspired by this I wrote *The challenge of bird sounds* for Birding World (Constantine 1994), and this guide is an expanded and illustrated development of the ideas presented in that paper.

Since 2000 I have worked with Arnoud van den Berg and Magnus Robb ('The Sound Approach') on the ambitious undertaking of recording all the sounds of birds in the Western Palearctic; they, along with Dick Forsman and Killian, have travelled the world recording birds and noting age, sex and the circumstances in which the sounds were made. They have then challenged every thought and proved and disproved some of the theories that I have read. Many are taken from the superb *Ecology and evolution of acoustic communication in birds* edited by Donald Kroodsma & Edward Miller (1996).

The recordings used in this guide are taken from the 30 000 or so amassed by The Sound Approach since 2000, and many were collected especially to illustrate this book. They were made with stereo microphones, and recorded digitally, without compression. Editing has been kept to a minimum and, unless stated otherwise, natural gaps between sounds are the same length as in the original recordings. Where necessary, recordings have been equalised to minimise distracting background sounds such as wind and traffic. Dates and locations are always noted, as are time of day and the age and sex of the birds, if known. Where ageing and sexing was difficult, the recordist has often worked with a second observer to make this possible. In quiet surroundings we have sometimes been able to use different microphones that create superb stereo imaging. We recommend that you use good quality headphones for the best listening experience.

The book is written in the first person although parts have been written by other members of The Sound Approach, particularly Magnus. The English names follow Dutch Birding guidelines (van den Berg 2006), as Arnoud is the editor, and despite these considerable contributions any mistakes and inconsistencies are my own. Originally, when working on the idea of a 'sound approach', I tried to simplify everything. I wanted to popularise the sound approach to birding and believed that drawing up and explaining a series of 'rules', to be applied consistently to all situations, would best achieve this. I have learnt that bird sound is gloriously varied and more astonishing than any plumage. With such a subject it was easy to go on and on reading, birding and recording and that is my excuse for having allowed many years to pass. Now it is time to try to provide the vocabulary and biological background needed to bridge the gap between bird sounds and the much better known visual aspect of birding.

Part 1: 'I don't do calls'

Crossing the sound barrier

Help in understanding bird sounds and developing skills to recognise them is hard to come by. Birders' conversations about identification typically revolve around plumage colours, structural features and so on. Similarly, field guides and birding journals tend to concentrate more on visible features than on vocalisations. It is not unusual for entire issues of the more popular journals and magazines to contain no reference to calls or songs at all, a surprising fact when one considers just how much an alert birder can achieve by listening. Consequently, the ways birders identify and describe bird sounds tend to be haphazard and confused. It's frustrating to read long-winded disputes about the identity of a particular rarity on the internet, with numerous photographs to look at, when a sound recording would have settled the matter in a moment. If considered at all, the role of sounds in identification often goes little further than noting the general tone of voice. Because of a lack of generally shared and understood terms, it is notoriously difficult to describe to someone else why a bird was what you heard it to be. This creates a situation where a large number of birders simply 'don't do calls'.

My own interest in learning and transcribing bird sounds first became obsessive in 1990. As a member of the *Transatlantic Vagrants*, along with Ian Hodgson, Bruce Mactavish, Anthony McGeehan and Killian Mullarney, I had to try to familiarise myself with the sounds of over 100 unfamiliar species in order to play a useful part in the *World Series of Birding* race in New Jersey, USA. Intense listening to recordings and attempts to learn calls and songs, using various mnemonics, birdie talk (*lui, lui, lui* etc), and comparisons with familiar European bird sounds merged into a technique which Newfoundland birder Bruce Mactavish summed up succinctly as "if it works for you". As I painstakingly noted *wop bop a deeeee* for Red-winged Blackbird *Agelaius phoeniceus* and *de-diddle, de-diddle, de-diddle* for Common Yellowthroat *Geothlypis trichas*, I realised that actually, despite its

Transatlantic Vagrants preparing for the World Series of Birding (from left Mark Constantine, Bruce Mactavish and Anthony McGeehan), Cape May, New Jersey, USA, 13 May 1993 *(Arnoud B van den Berg)*

American Golden Plover *Pluvialis dominica*, Kougarok road, Nome, Seward Peninsula, Alaska, USA, 1 June 2004 *(René Pop)*

charms, this approach didn't work for me. Such wonderfully rich sounds usually didn't take well to being 'dumbed down' in this way. Many common European bird sounds are easy to transcribe, and have become enshrined in birders' vocabularies, with *cuckoo, hoopoe,* and *too-whit too-woo* being among the most enduring and successful. However, the majority of bird sounds are too complex and varied for such simple transcriptions. Try coming up with a catchy one for Common Blackbird *Turdus merula* song, for example. The rich variety of its song repertoire simply won't allow it. At the other extreme, this approach runs into great difficulties when tackling a range of simple but very similar sounds that differ in rather subtle ways. How many written variations of *tak* are really helpful when trying to transcribe Western Palearctic warbler calls? Not to mention chats, flycatchers and many more species, all of which can give very similar-sounding calls.

Bird racing isn't to everyone's taste and, after the first year, Ian Hodgson left, followed by Killian two years later, and I took over as captain. Anthony and I then asked Arnoud to join the team. I knew Arnoud was editor of Dutch Birding and a bird photographer, but I didn't realise that he was also a bird sound recordist. In fact he had a lot of experience, and had provided Cornell University with over 4000 recordings from South America and south-eastern Asia. Over the next seven springs, he and I shared a room for the *World Series of Birding* fortnight, scouting by day and talking bird sounds by night. At the time he was busy translating Lars Jonsson's *Birds of Europe* (1992) into Dutch. We talked about the difficulties of describing bird sounds, and I tried to persuade him to join me in creating The Sound Approach.

Written descriptions in field guides tend to be of rather limited value. As an illustration of this, try asking an Englishman, an Irishman, a Scotsman and a Swede (the best selling European field guides have Swedish authors) to pronounce 'RSPB' and hear the differences in pronunciation. In the English version of the *Hamlyn guide* (Bruun, Delin & Svensson 1992) the commonest call of Sandwich Tern *Sterna sandvicensis* is described as *kee-yek*. In the original Swedish version of the *Collins bird guide* (Mullarney et al 1999) the same call is described as *krierjik!* Peter Grant's first English draft had *kerrick*, with the bold type for the second syllable added later: *kerrick*. In the meantime, Sandwich Terns are more than happy to surprise us with their own subtle variations.

Tone and timbre

The general character or quality of a bird's sounds is often described by the word *tone*, which might be thought of as a sound equivalent to visual *jizz* from a military abbreviation for 'general impression of size and shape' of an airplane. *Timbre* is a more specific word for the texture or spectral colour of a sound (squeaky, buzzing, shrill etc), independent of its pitch or rhythm, and is best pronounced *taamber* with a touch of French nasal timbre. Describing *tone* or *timbre*, whether it is the general character of a bird's voice, or just one particular note, is as hard as describing a colour, a smell or a taste. Bruun, Delin & Svensson (1992), in their excellent text for the *Hamlyn guide*, use over 120 different adjectives in a valiant attempt to convey these qualities. There are some wonderful metaphors too: staying with Sandwich Tern, my favourite is the description of its call sounding "like amalgam being pressed into a tooth", which was used again by Lars Svensson in the *Collins bird guide*. Such colourful descriptions are worth attempting, but in practise few of us have the poetic talent to match them.

Pacific Golden Plover *Pluvialis fulva*, Tacumshin, Wexford, Ireland, 16 July 1988 *(Killian Mullarney)*

To illustrate the problems writers of field guides experience, listen to the first track on the accompanying CD1. Then try using adjectives to describe the calls these *Pluvialis* plovers made when taking off and flying away **(CD1-01)**. David Sibley, in his ground-breaking *North American bird guide* (2000), describes Grey Plover *P squatarola* as "melancholy" and European Golden Plover *P apricaria* as "plaintive", which then leaves him with "sad-sounding" for American Golden Plover *P dominica*. When it comes to Pacific Golden Plover *P fulva*, he has run out of emotive adjectives altogether.

Grey Plover *Pluvialis squatarola* Lena delta, Yakutia, Russia, c 04:00, 10 June 2004. Typical calls of an adult in flight over its tundra breeding territory, recorded at close range. Background: another Grey Plover singing. 04.026.MR.10030.11 **CD1-01a** 0:00 - 0:15

European Golden Plover *Pluvialis apricaria* Griend, Friesland, Netherlands, 11 September 2005. Typical calls of a migrant juvenile when flushed, recorded on a tiny uninhabited island in the Wadden Sea. Background: Eurasian Oystercatcher *Haematopus ostralegus* and Eurasian Curlew *Numenius arquata*. 05.025.MR.05037.00 **CD1-01b** 0:17 - 0:31

American Golden Plover *Pluvialis dominica* Tacumshin Lake, Wexford, Ireland, 28 August 2002. An adult, flushed. One of many subtle variations that can be heard in flight. Background: Common Redshank *Tringa totanus*. 02.040.MR.00145.00 **CD1-01c** 0:33 – 0:51

Pacific Golden Plover *Pluvialis fulva* Tacumshin Lake, Wexford, Ireland, 08:50, 2 August 2005. Several calls of a first-summer bird on being flushed, each one of which is different, and intriguing. Be careful with American and Pacific Golden Plovers as they can sound very similar. Background: Herring Gull *Larus argentatus*. 05.001.KM.14825.11 **CD1-01d** 0:53 – 1:03

Such examples could be seen as mildly entertaining if the combination of all these communication problems did not create such difficulty. *The birds of the Western Palearctic* ('BWP'), in its first volume's introduction (Cramp & Simmons 1977), has two and a half pages of frustrated comments on the vagaries of described bird sound. As one of the very few European publications to give so much space to bird vocalisations, it is sad when the editors sum it all up as "groping towards communication", and go on, "even this has been frustrated by uncertainty over the intention of the writer of an original description, and whether his chosen words accurately conveyed his intention". Even with the electronic versions of BWP, the bird recordings referred to in the text are not the ones provided for listening, although a few can be found in *British bird sounds* on CD (Kettle 1992).

Pitch and frequency

To understand hearing and the subtleties of identifying different bird sounds, one has to learn about sound frequencies. This is as fundamental to describing sounds as size assessment is to descriptions of appearance. Put simply, frequency is a measure of the number of sound waves occurring during a given stretch of time. **High frequencies create sounds we hear as 'high-pitched', and low frequencies sounds we hear as 'low-pitched'.**

Trying to assess the frequency of a sound often highlights the limitations of our individual hearing. Many of us experience some hearing-loss during our lifetime, just as many suffer from short- and long-sightedness, or colour-blindness. This most commonly occurs with age, as a loss of perception of high-pitched sounds. As a general rule, young girls have the best high frequency hearing, older women next, then young men and finally older men. It shouldn't interfere with sound identification, although it is good to know what one's strengths and weaknesses are. As I have grown older, I have found it gradually more difficult to hear Goldcrest *Regulus regulus* calls and the song of Common Grasshopper Warbler *Locustella naevia* at a distance. This loss of high frequency hearing is more noticeable in situations other than birding. For example, most people would probably notice that they are unable to understand speech clearly in a noisy pub before they find that they cannot hear a Goldcrest calling. Another of the reasons why bird sounds can be difficult to hear is that they are often not very powerful sounds. Personally, I find as compensation that I can often hear distant low-frequency sounds like a Great Bittern's *Botaurus stellaris* boom or the low and relatively weak hoot of a Long-eared Owl *Asio otus*, long before my high frequency hearing birding

colleagues. One of North America's finest sound recordists, Lang Elliott, who recorded most of the sounds on the excellent *Stokes field guide* (Elliott et al 1997), has also never been able to hear high frequencies.

Everyone's ability to hear can be temporarily affected by, for example, a heavy cold, changes in air pressure during a recent airplane flight, exposure to loud noise at a club or loud concert and, more obviously, hats and ear coverings. Like our other senses, our hearing is best by mid-morning and is poor in the early morning and later in the day through tiredness or lack of concentration. For both birds and humans, the subtle differences in timing and loudness between the different versions of a sound reaching each ear allow us to pinpoint the direction a sound is coming from. Some people are partly deaf in one ear (one in 100), and this type of deafness will cause difficulty in determining the direction that a sound is coming from.

It is more important for us birders to understand what we hear rather than focus on variations in physical hearing ability, as difficulties registering and describing what is heard have more to do with *comprehension* and *vocabulary*. These skills come with time, training and experience.

Whereas frequency is a measurement, in Hertz (Hz), of sound wave cycles per second (1000 per second makes one kilohertz or 1 kHz), pitch is a word used to describe how you hear this. So, frequency and pitch are not quite the same. A bat's sonar and an elephant's subsonic rumbles for example, have measurable frequencies, but as long as they are beyond our range of hearing they have no pitch that is audible to a human. Despite these limitations, the human ear can receive a wide range of frequencies, and a pair in good working order can register frequencies from as low as 20 Hz up to around 20 kHz. At high and low extremes, a sound must be very loud for us to be able to hear it. Our hearing is at its most sensitive between 400 Hz and 3 kHz, a range roughly equivalent to the upper half of the piano, and we are less able to discriminate between sounds the further they are from the middle of our hearing range. Fortunately, our hearing is more than adequate for bird sounds, the majority of which actually fall within our most sensitive range. Even bird vocalisations that go above that do not actually go much higher than 8 kHz, and are well within most people's upper hearing limit.

When musicians say they have 'perfect pitch', they are referring to the ability to identify or reproduce an exact pitch - say 'middle C' (262 Hz) - without recourse to a reference pitch such as a note on the piano. It is quite a rare ability, and by no means the only benchmark for a 'good ear'. Many famous composers including Maurice Ravel, Igor Stravinsky and Richard Wagner did not have it, and you can certainly identify bird sounds without having this ability.

Telling a listening companion which part of the sound spectrum they should concentrate on is as important a clue for picking out a sound as directions ("just left of the buoy") are for a visual target. We have chosen a set of recordings to illustrate the broad range of different frequencies that birds use (**CD1-02**). A kind of *doh ray me* of bird sound, from the foghorn-like depths of the Great Bittern to some amazingly high, almost bat-like notes in the song of Lesser Whitethroat *Sylvia curruca*.

Great Bittern *Botaurus stellaris* Weerribben, Overijssel, Netherlands, 22:50, 4 May 2003. After a series of faint *up* sounds as it gulps air, this male gives five loud 'booms', foghorn-like sounds around **167 Hz**. Before each boom we can hear a quieter, higher note at 200 Hz where the bird seems to be inhaling; the first boom is actually preceded by two of these plus a brief lower note at around 122 Hz. The five booms produced by this male are all of more or less the same strength, suggesting that it is in good condition and most likely an adult. Background: Marsh Frog *Rana ridibunda*. 03.013.MR.01115f.10
CD1-02a
0:00 – 0:20

Ural Owl *Strix uralensis*, Vällen area south of Harg, Uppland, Sweden, 23:00, 1 April 2006. This adult male concentrates most of its energy at around **370 Hz**. It sings in a silent, but resonant spruce forest. After a long gap, typical of many birds with such deep voices, it sings a second time. 06.004.MR.14030.00
CD1-02b
0:22 – 1:04

Common Cuckoo *Cuculus canorus* Białowieza forest, Podlaskie, Poland, 20:30, 3 May 2005. At dusk, a male perched on top of a spruce tests the forest acoustics with its song. The pitches of its two notes are at **570 Hz** and **520 Hz**, respectively. Background: Common Blackbird *Turdus merula* and Song Thrush *T philomelos*. 05.006.MR.04331.01
CD1-02c
1:06 – 1:25

Little Owl *Athene noctua* Itteren, Limburg, Netherlands, 21:08, 5 March 2002. A pair calling after dark; this is one of their most characteristic calls. The louder bird's calls are produced at around **1.2 kHz**. 02.001.AB.03911.11
CD1-02d
1:27 – 2:00

Common Redshank *Tringa totanus* Texel, Noord-Holland, Netherlands, 24 April 2003. Two individuals call *tyuuu* to each other from opposite sides of a pool. The long, sustained *uuu* part of the call is produced at **2.23 kHz**. Background: displaying Common Eider *Somateria mollissima*, Eurasian Oystercatcher *Haematopus ostralegus* and Black-tailed Godwit *Limosa limosa*. 03.011.MR.12220.21
CD1-02e
2:02 – 2:24

Common Sandpiper *Actitis hypoleucos* Skuleskogen, Ångermanland, Sweden, 09:58, 17 July 2001. At **4.8 kHz**, the sustained whistles of this nervous adult, heard from 8 sec into the recording, are just over twice as high as the *tyuuu* calls of Common Redshank heard in the preceding recording. 01.014.AB.03230.31
CD1-02f
2:26 – 2:48

Goldcrest *Regulus regulus* Hauts Plateaux du Vercors, Drôme, France, 10:54, 31 May 2002. The main frequency around which this adult male spins its cyclical song is **7 kHz**. Background: European Robin *Erithacus rubecula* and Coal Tit *Periparus ater*. 02.011.AB.05825.01
CD1-02g
2:49 – 3:22

Lesser Whitethroat *Sylvia curruca* 2000 m altitude, Geyik Daglari, Akseki, Turkey, 12 May 2001. During the very first second of the recording, before the main phrase starts, the bird produces two incredibly high notes at **11.7** and **12.3 kHz**, respectively! Similar notes are also present in the recording at 3:36 – 3:37. Background: Coal Tit *Periparus ater*. 01.019.MR.00926.01
CD1-02h
3:24 – 3:44

Listening casually to the song of this male Lesser Whitethroat, you might wonder what it is doing at the top of our scale. Most of its song is pitched well below the Goldcrest, with some notes as low as 1.6 kHz, but the introductory notes are the highest complete notes we have found. Having tested your equipment to the limits to hear the stratospheric tittering notes of Lesser Whitethroat, the reeling song of a Common Grasshopper Warbler (CD1-03) should no longer seem quite so high-pitched. Here it is compared to the lower-pitched reeling of a Savi's Warbler *L luscinioides* (CD1-04), a good example of pitch as the simplest means to distinguish the songs of two species. The song of Common Grasshopper is concentrated around 6 kHz, whereas Savi's is around 4 kHz.

CD1-03   **Common Grasshopper Warbler** *Locustella naevia* Dijkwielen, Wieringermeer, Noord-Holland, Netherlands, 03:30, 2 May 2003. Reeling song. Main frequency 6 kHz, pulse rate 24/sec. Background: Mallard *Anas platyrhynchos* and Common Tern *Sterna hirundo*. (See sonagram on page 103.) 03.003.MR.12240.01

CD1-04   **Savi's Warbler** *Locustella luscinioides* Karazhar field station, Aqmola Oblast, Kazakhstan, 14:00, 20 May 2003. Reeling song. Main frequency 4 kHz, pulse rate 48/sec. Background: Paddyfield Warbler *Acrocephalus agricola*. (See sonagram on page 102.) 03.017.MR.12852.00

Now, try a species-pair that illustrates rise and fall in pitch. These recordings of the typical year round calls of Common Ringed Plover *Charadrius hiaticula* (CD1-05) and Little Ringed Plover *C dubius* (CD1-06) illustrate upward and downward inflections, respectively. The Common Ringed is at a similar pitch to the Common Redshank in CD1-02e, but the Little Ringed is considerably higher.

Common Ringed Plover *Charadrius hiaticula* Tacumshin Lake, Wexford, Ireland, 3 September 2000. Upward-inflected calls of several birds. Background: a flock of quietly chattering Dunlin *Calidris alpina*. 00.001.KM.03813a.01   CD1-05

Little Ringed Plover *Charadrius dubius* Parc Natural S'Albufera, Mallorca, Spain, dusk, 1 April 2003. Downward-inflected calls of a breeding adult on being flushed. These calls are also higher-pitched and a third shorter than the equivalent calls of Common Ringed Plover in CD1-05. Background: Mallard *Anas platyrhynchos* and Zitting Cisticola *Cisticola juncidis*. 03.008.MR.02314.01   CD1-06

Interestingly, those high notes of Lesser Whitethroat aren't the only sound to test our hearing. Listen to the calls of a Red-throated Pipit *Anthus cervinus* in flight (CD1-07), the loudest parts of which are pitched as high as of a Goldcrest. A person who is less receptive to high frequency sound will hear and probably describe this call differently from someone with a wider range of hearing. Just as white light is composed of a rainbow of different colours, which can be separated by a prism, the sounds we hear are a blend of layers of sound. The lowest layer is called the 'fundamental'. Typically, the layers above the fundamental are at exact multiples of its frequency, in which case they are called 'harmonics' (or 'overtones'). Because the layers are related in this simple way, their sound waves melt together or harmonise, and we don't hear them as separate sounds. Together, they are responsible for the timbre of the sound, a 'nasal' sound having lots of harmonics, and a pure tone having none. Because high frequencies don't carry as far as low frequencies, the effect of the higher harmonics is reduced with distance, even for those with the best hearing.

Red-throated Pipit *Anthus cervinus* Seosan Lakes, Chungcheongnam-do, South Korea, 07:50, 14 October 2002. Calls of a passing migrant, flying away in a straight line. The calls later in the recording sound slightly less piercing. This is not only due to the sound being quieter from a distance: the harmonics also become weaker. Background: Tundra Bean Geese *Anser serrirostris*. 02.029.AB.11311.01   CD1-07

Apart from the effects of distance on volume and harmonics, another reason why the Red-throated Pipit calls change slightly as the bird flies away is the 'Doppler effect'. This phenomenon is the apparent shift in pitch as the source of a sound approaches (shorter wavelengths and higher frequency) or moves away (longer wavelengths and lower frequency). Think of a child describing a passing car: *eeeuooow!* The sound seems to change pitch, being higher as it approaches and lower as it moves away. The same can happen with a passing flock of geese, or a screaming flock of Common Swifts *Apus apus* or Pallid Swifts *A pallidus* flying past: as they get closer the pitch seems to rise, and as they fly away it seems to fall. Listen to the Doppler effect in the wingbeats of a passing pair of Mute Swans *Cygnus olor* (**CD1-08**). You can also hear their grunting calls.

CD1-08   **Mute Swan** *Cygnus olor* Poole Harbour, Dorset, England, 08:00, 18 January 2004. Wing sounds and some calls, gradually descending in pitch due to the Doppler effect, as a pair flies past. 04.002.MC.11730.00

Most birds are thought to have a hearing range similar to that of humans. Few are supposed to be able to hear frequencies above 20 kHz, and most birds' hearing is at its most sensitive between 1 kHz and 5 kHz (Dooling 1982). Owls are an exception, with greater sensitivity at higher frequencies (eg, Long-eared Owl at 6 kHz) where squeaking and rustling can be heard. In general, sounds that are ultrasonic or above the range of hearing for us can be assumed to be beyond the hearing of birds too, although a few birds can hear sounds that are infrasonic (below our lowest limit of hearing). Western Capercaillies *Tetrao urogallus* have an infrasound component in their song (Moss & Lockie 1979), and the Rock Dove *Columba livia* is even thought to be able to hear sounds lower than 1 Hz. When 60 000 English homing pigeons

were released in France in June 1997 and around a third of them were never seen again, it was suggested the birds lost their way after crossing the path of low frequency shock waves generated by the sonic boom from Concorde, which raises the question as to whether sound works for orientation instead of (or together with) earth magnetism.

When it comes to pitch perception in sound recordings, the equipment used is important to consider. Some basic microphones and recorders are incapable of recording higher frequencies, so they can miss crucial harmonics, or even those very high Lesser Whitethroat notes. At present something similar happens when you try playing bird sounds over the phone. Above a certain frequency (around 4 kHz) nothing at all is carried, so no matter how ear-splittingly loud you play the Goldcrest recording (CD1-02g) down the phone, it will not reach the listener at the other end. This will change as technology progresses into better phones. At the other extreme, really poor equipment might even add its own 'artefacts': distorting, harmonic-like sounds that were not present in the original.

Rhythm and timing

After pitch, the next consideration is the *rhythm* of the sound. The rhythmic pattern within individual songs or calls is of crucial importance in identifying bird sounds. Equally important is the rate at which a sound is delivered, and whether or not this is constant. This applies at different levels, including both the *tempo* of song or call delivery over a longer stretch of time, and how rapidly the notes of a particular chuckling or rattling sound are repeated. Bear in mind that the silent gaps between sounds can be as relevant as the sounds themselves. In everything from flight calls to complex songs, paying attention to rhythm can provide the key in recognising sounds.

Timing calls or songs in the field, or from recordings, can make it easier to recognise more subtle differences in rhythm. Sounds and the gaps between them can be timed with a stopwatch. Sometimes, just counting notes as fast as possible can give a useful, if rough, guide; it can be difficult to count more than six or seven notes in a second. Most call notes are over in a fraction of a second, so beware of over-estimating the length of a sound.

Living in Dorset, England, I get to hear a fair bit of European Reed Warbler *Acrocephalus scirpaceus* song (**CD1-09**), but a singing Sedge Warbler *A schoenobaenus* is something I encounter much less often. Their songs are superficially similar, and there are several ways to tell them apart, of which *tempo* - the rate of delivery of the song - is the best. European Reed Warbler plods along with a constant regularity, pacing itself for a long run without stopping, and even when it impersonates other birds (eg, calls of Common Chiffchaff *Phylloscopus collybita* and European Goldfinch *Carduelis carduelis* in this recording), it does so within the confines of its regular tempo. Sedge Warbler can also sing for a long time without stopping, but its tempo is more varied and faster (**CD1-10**). The song is higher-pitched on average, because it likes to launch itself briefly into rather high frequencies, just as it sometimes takes off on brief songflights.

Sedge Warbler *Acrocephalus schoenobaenus* Vendelsjön, Uppland, Sweden, 00:00, 19 July 2001. Song of a presumed male. Background: flight calls of Great Bittern *Botaurus stellaris*. 01.014.AB.14647.10   CD1-10

There are other ways in which aspects of rhythm and timing can be important in identifying bird sounds. At the most detailed level there is the pulse rate of rattles, trills and reeling sounds. The denser reeling in the song of Savi's Warbler (CD1-04) compared to Common Grasshopper Warbler (CD1-03) is actually due to a pulse which is twice as fast – about 48 per second in this particular Savi's and 25 per second in the Common Grasshopper. So not only is Savi's significantly lower-pitched; the individual pulses in its denser trill are much harder to discern.

Now try the two other *Locustella* warblers that breed in the Western Palearctic. Listen to the reeling of Lanceolated Warbler *L lanceolata* (**CD1-11**), which has a pulse rate slightly slower than Common Grasshopper Warbler, about 18 per second, resulting in a looser or weaker-sounding trill. Finally, the song of River Warbler *L fluviatilis* has a much slower pulse, in this recording only about 10 per second (**CD1-12**). It's so slow you can hardly call it 'reeling', and the individual pulses are easy to hear. The exact pulse rates of these *Locustella* songs may vary a little but the rule always holds that Savi's has the fastest pulse followed by Common Grasshopper, then Lanceolated, with River being the slowest.

CD1-09   **European Reed Warbler** *Acrocephalus scirpaceus* Wareham, Dorset, England, 04:15, 13 May 2000. Song of a presumed male, singing from an exposed perch. Its mate is nearby, collecting nest material. Background: Black-headed Gull *Larus ridibundus*, Eurasian Skylark *Alauda arvensis* and Meadow Pipit *Anthus pratensis*. 00.013.MC.02430.01

Lanceolated Warbler *Locustella lanceolata* Ruuppovaara, Kitee, Pohjois-Karjala, Finland, 03:20, 10 July 2003. Reeling, three very short songs. 03.004.DF.01927c.21   CD1-11

River Warbler *Locustella fluviatilis* Bieszczadi national park, Podkarpackie, Poland, 22:00, 13 June 2005. Several short songs. 05.015.MR.01142.01   CD1-12

Part 2: Put it all together and what have you got?

When you put timbre, pitch and timing together and give them a stir you get structure and syntax. It has taken me a full 15 years to realise that all the modern approaches to bird identification rely on structure. Moult, topography, biometrics: they are all about structure. Bird sound has structure but you can only see it in a sonagram. Learn to read a sonagram and you are on the road to success.

I learnt many American bird songs from Bruce over several years of competing in the *World Series of Birding* in New Jersey. He was very good with them, and it was a long time before it dawned on me that because we were well south of his native Newfoundland, he had little experience of many of the songs he was teaching me. "Sonagrams", he said when I asked him his secret. He had learnt the songs from the tiny sonagrams in the *Golden field guide* (Robbins et al 1983). Now I'm more familiar with them, it's still impressive. Not many people do it, but rather like a magician's trick, once you know how easy it is to do, you want to do it yourself.

Sonagrams are simply graphic illustrations of sound, in the same way that graphs can illustrate a company's share price. In these and many other kinds of graphs, the lower axis represents time, scanning from left to right. Instead of variations in share price, a sonagram traces the ups and downs of sounds across time. The higher on the page, the higher the pitch; the closer to the base line, the lower the pitch. That's it! Once you've grasped that, everything else is just a luxury.

Most published sonagrams are produced at compatible scales. In this book, we have made them with a scale from 0 to 8 kHz on the vertical frequency axis, or from 0 to 12 kHz when we wanted to include very high frequency sounds. In two further instances we have used 6 kHz and 16 kHz scales to show low and even higher sounds, respectively. In the days before personal computers, published sonagrams tended to cover 2 to 4 seconds on the horizontal time axis, because this was approximately one turn of the cylinder of the original Kay Sona-Graph. Nowadays, to fit everything in without a squeeze, the time on the horizontal can be as long or as short as needed. We have used a variety of time scales throughout the book, but taken care to ensure that sonagrams being compared are at exactly the same scale. As extras, we use colours to help in interpreting the sonagrams, and we can magnify some details to take a closer look. Simple warbler calls are a good start when learning sonagrams. In these four examples of various *Phylloscopus* warblers, the first has an upward inflection, the second upwards with a kink, the third is flat and the last has a downward inflection.

Magnus, cows and Baillon's Crake *Porzana pusilla*, Polder Achteraf, Noord-Holland, Netherlands, 18 August 2005 *(Phil Koken)*. One bird of the pair with young on CD1-43.

Simple calls

This first sonagram shows *huit* calls of a Common Chiffchaff (**CD1-13**), regularly used by adults. Each call has three layers, and all of them start low to the left and end high to the right, so the call rises in pitch. The three layers are, from the bottom up, the fundamental, first harmonic and second harmonic. These add a little 'colour' to the sound, a slight impurity which is very hard to describe, but very easy to hear and see.

The corresponding call of a Willow Warbler *P trochilus* in the next sonagram was recorded when Magnus and Roy Slaterus were looking for a Hazel Grouse *Bonasa bonasia* beside the Siemianowka reservoir in north-eastern Poland (**CD1-14**). This sonagram shows a single, weak harmonic; compared to the chiffchaff's call this is a purer-sounding whistle. Look at the sonagram and listen for the sudden rise in pitch at the end. This is the best way to tell a Willow Warbler's from a Common Chiffchaff's call.

CD1-13 **Common Chiffchaff** *Phylloscopus collybita collybita* Lascowiec, Podlaskie, Poland, 18:30, 1 May 2005. Calling from deep in roadside bushes, one of two birds. Background: European Robin *Erithacus rubecula*, Willow Warbler *Phylloscopus trochilus* and Common Chaffinch *Fringilla coelebs*. 05.005.MR.14636.01

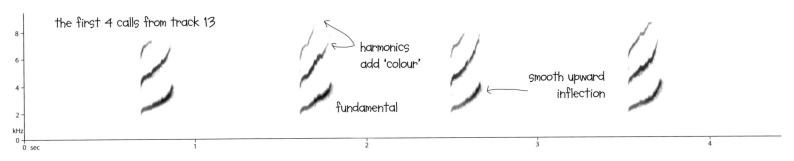

CD1-14 **Willow Warbler** *Phylloscopus trochilus* Siemianowka, Podlaskie, Poland, 20:30, 16 June 2005. Typical calls of a bird foraging at dusk. Background: Common Blackbird *Turdus merula*, Song Thrush *T philomelos* and Great Reed Warbler *Acrocephalus arundinaceus*. 05.015.MR.12835.01

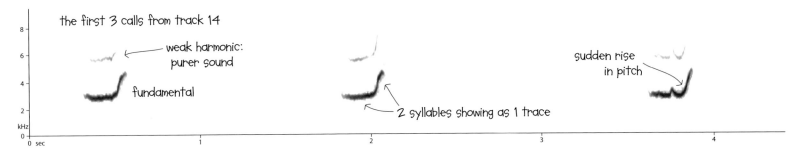

Next comes the sonagram of the equivalent calls of wintering Siberian Chiffchaff *P c tristis* recorded at Bharatpur in India (**CD1-15**). You won't see any clear inflection in pitch: the sound is flat. These distinctive calls are quite high-pitched, and their harmonics are much less prominent, so when you listen to the recording, you will hear that the tone is a much purer-sounding whistle.

These typical calls of Iberian Chiffchaff *P ibericus* (**CD1-16**) were recorded in a beautiful pine forest along the ancient pilgrim's path to Santiago de Compostela in north-western Spain. They are distinguished from calls of other chiffchaffs occurring in western Europe by their smooth downward inflection. These calls start at a higher pitch, more or less where the others finish, then drop to where the Willow Warbler starts.

CD1-15   **Siberian Chiffchaff** *Phylloscopus collybita tristis* Keoladeo Ghana national park, Bharatpur, Rajasthan, India, 15 January 2002. Typical calls of a bird wintering in bushes along a ditch. Background: juvenile Painted Storks *Mycteria leucocephala* on the nest. 02.002.MR.11934.01

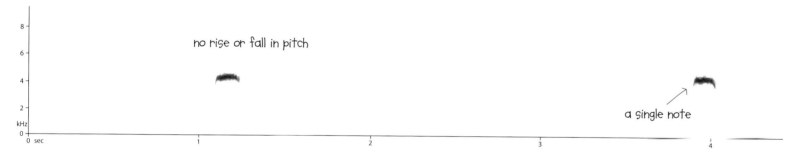

CD1-16   **Iberian Chiffchaff** *Phylloscopus ibericus* Erro, Navarra, Spain, 09:19, 26 June 2002. An adult that had been feeding fledged young, calling in open mixed woods with quite a lot of pines on a high hill ridge. Background: Common Wood Pigeon *Columba palumbus*, Winter Wren *Troglodytes troglodytes* and Common Chaffinch *Fringilla coelebs*. 02.026.AB.04133.01

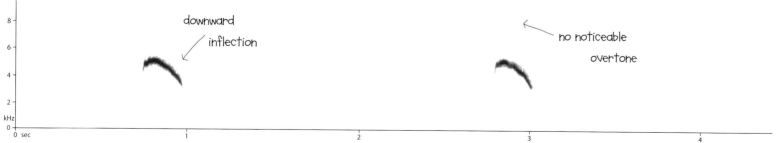

Simple song

The first time I realised that I could make my own sonagrams on a lap-top computer I had this shown to me by Swedish birders, Lars Jonsson and Urban Olsson, at the 1993 conference on English bird names organised by Birding World at Swanwick in Derbyshire, England. Urban took his Mac from the hotel safe and Lars whistled the song of a Common Rosefinch *Carpodacus erythrinus* (**CD-17**) into its mic, and then Urban produced a sonagram. In this case, we've had to make do with a real Common Rosefinch as we can no longer afford Lars and Urban. The simple traces on the sonagram are typical of the way song phrases show up on a page.

Inspired by this, I bought a Mac lap-top, and was producing my own sonagrams a short time later. I won't pretend I found it easy, but it was very satisfying. It meant I could make sound recordings in the field, analyse them at home, and compare them with published recordings and sonagrams. Difficult identifications could be confirmed within hours. If you have a go,

don't forget to use the same scale when comparing any two sonagrams. Once I had started to learn how to use the computer to produce sonagrams, I wanted to use it to answer all the other birding mysteries. What was the difference between Richard's *A richardi*, Blyth's *A godlewskii* and Tawny Pipit *A campestris* flight calls? What about Blyth's Reed *A dumetorum*, Marsh *A palustris* and European Reed Warbler calls? Siberian Stonechat *Saxicola maurus*? Semipalmated Plover *C semipalmatus*? How did the different gulls sound, and what could I see in their sonagrams? I can't quite remember how I first started talking to Paul Holt about it all, but I do remember that he had quite a few of these precious recordings that weren't available on *'Teach yourself bird sounds'*. Blyth's Pipit flight calls and a variety of Yellow-browed Warbler *P inornatus* sounds come to mind. But even he didn't have most of the desired recordings, and we started to talk about a new project, dreaming about collecting all these exciting sounds and publishing something. He came up with the name 'The Sound Approach', which with his Burnley vowels seemed to have a *w* where the *u* is. Then he went birding in China and hardly came home again.

CD1-17   **Common Rosefinch** *Carpodacus erythrinus* Täktom, Hanko, Uusimaa, Finland, 08:30, 2 July 2003. Song of an adult male. Background: Common Chaffinch *Fringilla coelebs*. 03.003.DF.13035.11

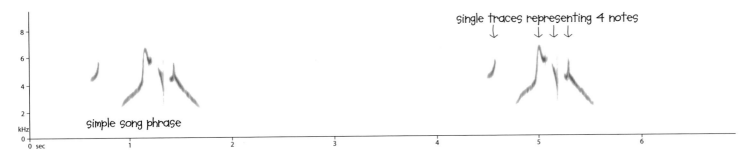

Now The Sound Approach has many of the recordings Paul and I craved back then, and Magnus and I have chosen a few of our favourites, some intriguing and some just rare examples that illustrate different types of sonagram and, I hope, take bird sound identification a little further. Being able to see small features you hadn't noticed just through listening is one of the advantages of looking at sonagrams.

'Curlews' and proportions in sonagrams

Sitting out at dusk drinking red wine and listening to Stone-curlews *Burhinus oedicnemus* on a Mediterranean island in the spring, has to be one of the great pleasures in the world. Even more so for sound buffs, for whom noises of the night are always an attraction. The secretive Stone-curlews are often hidden in an

orchard or deep grass during the day, and surprise when they call to each other straight after darkness falls. They have varied repertoires and at home, before I had as much experience, I mistook them for Eurasian Oystercatchers *Haematopus ostralegus*, Eurasian Curlew *Numenius arquata* and Little Owl *Athene noctua*. The first call they usually give after sunset is the one that gave them their name. Comparing these two sonagrams shows you the difference in proportions between the commonly heard and sometimes confused sounds of Eurasian Curlew with those of the unrelated Stone-curlew. You can see (and hear) that Eurasian Curlew starts with a long, low note and ends with a short high one (**CD1-18**), whereas Stone-curlew is the opposite, starting with a short lower one and with a longer, high note at the end (**CD1-19**).

Eurasian Curlew *Numenius arquata* Slikken van Bommenede, Zeeland, Netherlands, 20:30, 10 April 2005. Well-spaced *currrli* calls of a single bird flying over. This individual was not sexed but nearly all of the birds passing through on this date were females. Can be heard after dark. Background: Common Shelduck *Tadorna tadorna*, Kentish Plover *Charadrius alexandrinus*, Common Snipe *Gallinago gallinago*, Sandwich Tern *Sterna sandvicensis* and Willow Warbler *Phylloscopus trochilus*. 05.002.MR.11853.01

Stone-curlew *Burhinus oedicnemus* Kalloni salt pans, Lesvos, Greece, 15 April 2002. Typical *cr-leee* calls at close range, with some more complex calls of a second bird. Normally heard after dark. Background: Crested Lark *Galerida cristata*, Tree Pipit *Anthus trivialis* and Corn Bunting *Emberiza calandra*. 02.003.KM.12159.01

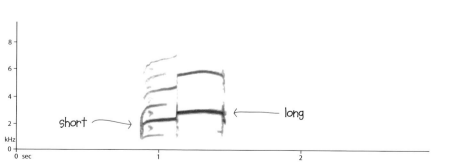

Kite and pipit calls illustrate modulation

Red Kite *Milvus milvus* are migrants in Schwaben, Bayern, Germany, and the locals look forward to their return in the way other Europeans wait for Common Cuckoo *Cuculus canorus*. I stayed with Diana Krautter who can whistle the 'Milan' into circling her as she watches from her garden. This bird was following the plough and calling to passing birds. The modulation in this Red Kite's call (**CD1-20**) is very slow and easy to hear (*aye aye aye*) and visible in the sonagram.

This Black-eared Kite *M lineatus* (**CD1-21**) was recorded in the north of Japan where in winter many roost on the edge of frozen lakes. Japanese fishermen carve fishing holes in the ice and the kites hope for scraps. They often mob the Steller's Sea Eagles *Haliaeetus pelagicus* and White-tailed Eagles *H albicilla* as they all look for fish remains. This note has a much faster modulation that sounds like a neigh of a horse.

CD1-20   **Red Kite** *Milvus milvus* Near Bodensee, Germany, 17:00, 31 May 2005. Calling while following the plough. Background: House Sparrow *Passer domesticus* and Common Chaffinch *Fringilla coelebs*. 05.012.MC.01220.31

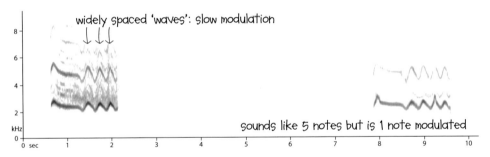

CD1-21   **Black-eared Kite** *Milvus lineatus* Nimuro, Hokkaido, Japan, 9 February 2005. Calling just after dawn. Background: a pair of Steller's Sea Eagles *Haliaeetus pelagicus* and some Jungle Crows *Corvus macrorhynchos japonensis*. 05.001.MC.04928.02

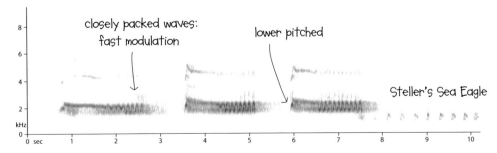

The flight sounds of Richard's, Tawny and Blyth's Pipits are like three quizzes with beginner, intermediate and advanced: Richard's Pipit has a diagnostic call used in flight that makes it very good to learn. Let's call it *squonk*. The great thing about Richard's Pipit is that when it passes overhead you can hear it coming a long way off and disappearing for quite a while so you can get your mind around the sound (**CD1-22**). This sound doesn't vary much; it can be given singly or in twos or threes, and most of the variation you hear is caused by distance. As you can see, sonagrams give us several additional characters to look and listen for. In this case, how 'buzzy' it sounds is a reflection on the modulations in the call: much faster than either of the kites. The buzzy quality is especially coarse and obvious in Richard's, where this has pronounced modulation, showing as 'shark's teeth' on a sonagram.

CD1-22   **Richard's Pipit** *Anthus richardi* IJmuiden, Noord-Holland, Netherlands, 09:04, 29 October 2005. Typical calls of a bird migrating along the Dutch coast: *squonk*. Background: European Robin *Erithacus rubecula*, Goldcrest *Regulus regulus*, Great Tit *Parus major*, European Blue Tit *Cyanistes caeruleus* and Common Chaffinch *Fringilla coelebs*. 05.029.MR.11126.23

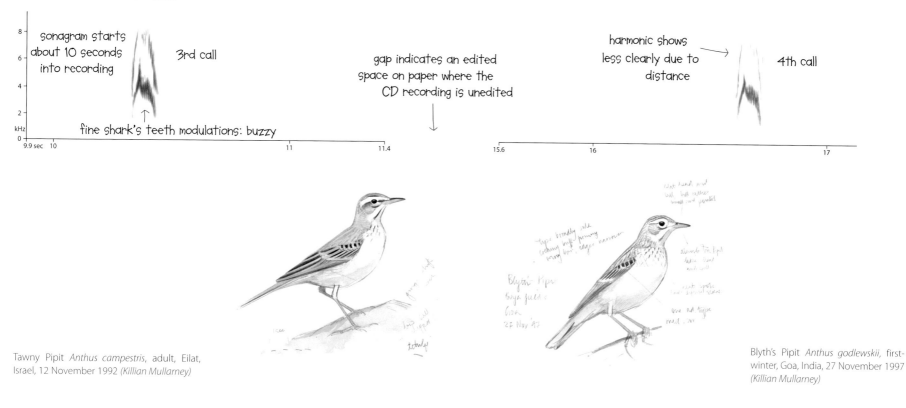

Tawny Pipit *Anthus campestris*, adult, Eilat, Israel, 12 November 1992 *(Killian Mullarney)*

Blyth's Pipit *Anthus godlewskii*, first-winter, Goa, India, 27 November 1997 *(Killian Mullarney)*

Tawny Pipits can be a little trickier, as they show a lot more variation (**CD1-23**). The next two recordings were made by Killian whose field notes describe the equivalent call of Tawny as "a strongly downslurred *tsleeuu*, a fuller, slightly longer note than a similar call of House Sparrow, reminiscent of Yellow Wagtail but not really confusable with it". This is the call he associates most with birds in full flight; "flushed birds may give it too, but it is often preceded or interspersed with a rapid series *tchilp-tchelp-*

tchilp.. notes, not unlike the usual take-off call of Short-toed Lark". Now check the sonagram; first notice the variation in sounds, the downslurred shape of the sound, then the pitch compared to Richard's Pipit. In Tawny's *tsleeuu* the modulated bits are so brief that they have very little bearing on the timbre of the call as a whole, leaving the sound slightly musical as an attractive note, or as Killian referred to it "a real call".

CD1-23a   **Tawny Pipit** *Anthus campestris* Sohar Sun Farms, Al Batinah, Oman. 27 October 2003. *Tsleeuu* calls of a bird in flight. 03.016.KM.05500.02
0:00-0:10

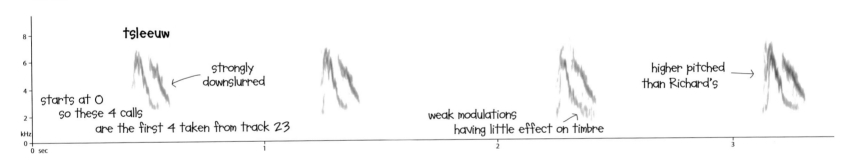

CD1-23b   **Tawny Pipit** *Anthus campestris* Sohar Sun Farms, Al Batinah, Oman. 20 October 2003. Two types of calls on flushing, a single *tsleeuu*, then a series of short *chip* calls.
0:11-0:16   Background of both recordings: Crested Lark *Galerida cristata*. 03.014.KM.13135.12

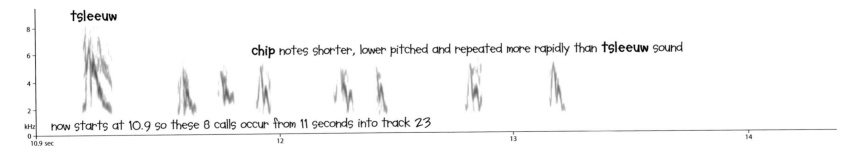

One of the reasons Blyth's Pipit counts as advanced is that it's extremely rare throughout the Western Palearctic, and consequently much sought after. Like Tawny Pipit, Blyth's has a variety of sounds it uses in flight (CD1-24). Comparing Blyth's to Tawny, Killian added: "most of the time it's just an unobtrusive and extremely Tawny Pipit-like *typp typp typp typp* every half second or so. If you are lucky enough to hear the full call, when it gets into its stride, its *squonk* equivalent is an emphatic *speuu*, a little higher-pitched than Richard's". You can see this on the sonagram and that the modulation is so rapid and fine that it results in a wheezing quality, or as Killian describes "not so throaty as Richard's, cleaner, more like Yellow Wagtail".

CD1-24   **Blyth's Pipit** *Anthus godlewskii* Baga fields, Goa, India, 16:00, 10 November 2001. First longer *speuu* calls, then short calls like *chip* of Tawny Pipit. Background: House Crow *Corvus splendens.* 01.011.KM.02835.01 & 01.011.KM. 03900.01

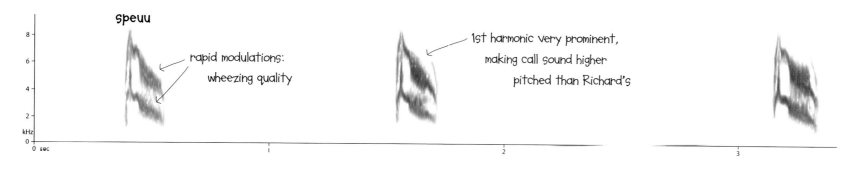

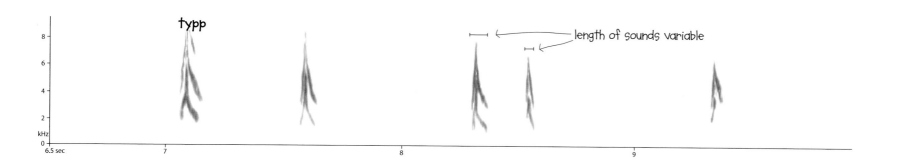

Broadband and Trumpeter Finches

Having looked at modulations, time for some fun. In the first sonagrams of the book, we already noted that adding layers of harmonics to a simple, pure-sounding linear whistle changes the timbre, but what happens when this is taken to extremes? When we started The Sound Approach, one of the most exciting prospects was to make recordings of Western Palearctic species that had never been included in audio publications before. Mongolian Finch *Bucanetes mongolicus* was one of these. It has various songs, and the most lyrical one recorded at the ruined Ishak Pasha palace in eastern Turkey near the border with Iran

(CD1-25) sounds like a cross between a Common Linnet *C cannabina* and a Common Rosefinch. In the sonagram you can see several layers of harmonics, giving it a somewhat squeaky timbre, but this is nothing compared to the amazing timbre of a Trumpeter Finch *B githagineus*, its desert counterpart (**CD1-26**). This was recorded in India in January 2002, close to the Pakistani border, with the two countries on the brink of war and Magnus trying to look unobtrusive, despite the parabola in hand, every time a military vehicle passed by. The Trumpeter Finch sounds as if he saw the funny side of all this. Look at the incredible profusion of layers in the sonagram: this cool little desert creature has been into 'broadband' for thousands of years.

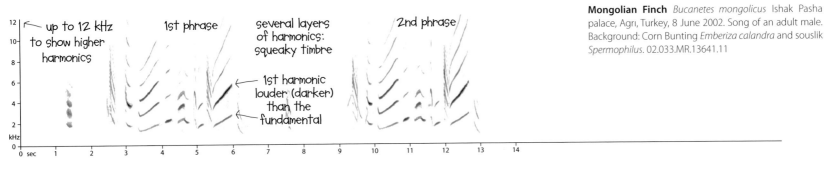

Mongolian Finch *Bucanetes mongolicus* Ishak Pasha palace, Ağrı, Turkey, 8 June 2002. Song of an adult male. Background: Corn Bunting *Emberiza calandra* and souslik *Spermophilus*. 02.033.MR.13641.11   **CD1-25**

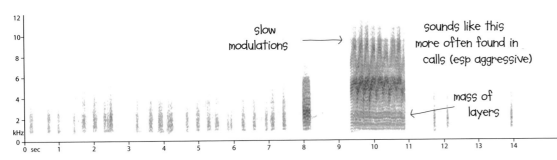

Trumpeter Finch *Bucanetes githagineus* Wood Fossil Park, Jaisalmer, Rajasthan, India, 24 January 2002. Song of an adult male. Background: Common Babbler *Turdoides caudatus*. 02.005.MR.04255.03   **CD1-26**

Shapes and Yellow-browed comparisons

Few people get Yellow-browed Warblers in their garden, so Arnoud was lucky when he recorded this one in a Bird Cherry *Prunus padus* in his garden at Santpoort-Zuid, the Netherlands **(CD1-27)**. Compare the sonagram with one of a Coal Tit *Periparus ater* recorded at nearby IJmuiden, as it perched briefly before continuing on a migration flight **(CD1-28)**. These two sounds are commonly confused; both are high-pitched and show a V-shape in sonagrams. As you can see, however, the Coal Tit's calls are a shorter, more rounded V-shape and it tends to double its calls, whereas the Yellow-browed does not. Now compare both to a Pallas's Leaf Warbler *P proregulus* recorded by Arnoud, surrounded by curious children, in the middle of town near Rotterdam **(CD1-29)**. The harmonics you can see in the sonagram create a similar quality to chiffchaff, but the rapid descent at the start, gives it a more of a *t-* or *ch-* sound. Both these qualities also separate it from Yellow-browed and Coal, and it is also lower-pitched. All a bit technical? Try Anthony's and

Yellow-browed Warbler *Phylloscopus inornatus*, first-winter, in suburban garden at Santpoort-Zuid, Noord-Holland, Netherlands, 7 October 2000 *(Arnoud B van den Berg)*. Same bird as on CD1-27.

Killian's more artful description, dreamt up when they first heard Pallas's Leaf Warbler in China; they compared Pallas's calls to "the twang sound when you skid a piece of ice across a frozen pond".

CD1-27   **Yellow-browed Warbler** *Phylloscopus inornatus* Santpoort-Zuid, Noord-Holland, Netherlands, 15:05, 7 October 2000. Typical calls by a first-winter migrant recorded in, less typically, a suburban garden 6 km inland. Background: Great Tit *Parus major*. 00.009.AB.04333.01

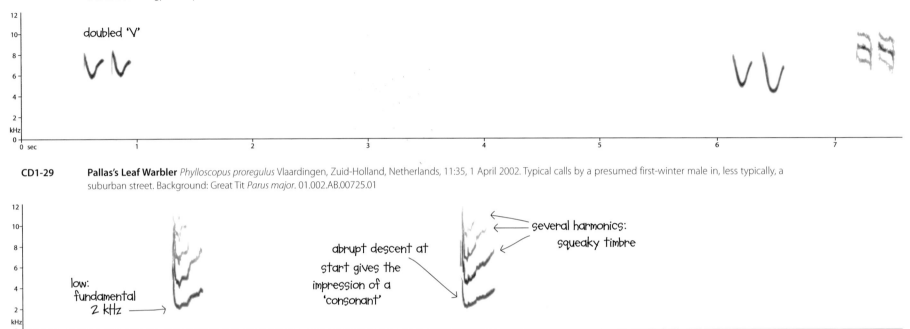

CD1-28 **Coal Tit** *Periparus ater* IJmuiden, Noord-Holland, Netherlands, 21 September 2005. Calls of two birds perched briefly in a willow before continuing on their migration flight. The birds were heading north, part of an invasion that allegedly originated in central Europe. Background: Dunnock *Prunella modularis*, European Blue Tit *Cyanistes caeruleus* and Eurasian Magpie *Pica pica*. 05.025.MR.15406.02

doubled 'V'

CD1-29 **Pallas's Leaf Warbler** *Phylloscopus proregulus* Vlaardingen, Zuid-Holland, Netherlands, 11:35, 1 April 2002. Typical calls by a presumed first-winter male in, less typically, a suburban street. Background: Great Tit *Parus major*. 01.002.AB.00725.01

low: fundamental 2 kHz

abrupt descent at start gives the impression of a 'consonant'

several harmonics: squeaky timbre

M shapes in Common Ringed and Semipalmated

In the summer of 2004, we sent Magnus to Siberia, Russia. He liked it so much he missed his plane home and had to wait five days for the next one. This gave him the opportunity to make lots of Common Ringed Plover recordings. A few weeks earlier, Arnoud travelling with René Pop through Alaska, USA, found, photographed and sound recorded a Semipalmated Plover

sitting beside the old road from Nome to the Eskimo village of Teller. Look at the sonagram as you listen to the sounds. These Common Ringed calls (**CD1-30**) have a simple rising inflection as you can see. In Semipalmated, the equivalent call is higher-pitched, has stronger inflections, and is M-shaped with a downward dip in the middle (**CD1-31**). Looking at the sonagram and listening to the CD does really help in understanding these differences but it is hard to put them into words.

CD1-30   **Common Ringed Plover** *Charadrius hiaticula tundrae* Tiksi, Yakutia, Russia, 2 July 2004. Calls of 'flight call' type; an adult standing its ground on its breeding territory. Background: Common Snipe *Gallinago gallinago*, Coues's Arctic Redpoll *Carduelis hornemanni exilipes* and Snow Bunting *Plectrophenax nivalis*. 04.036.MR.10124.01

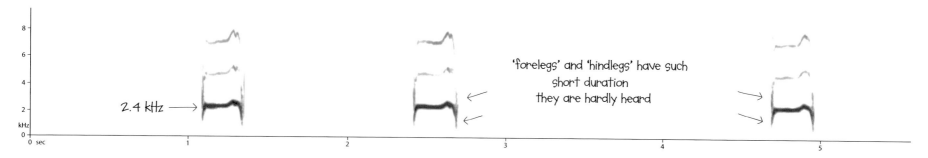

'forelegs' and 'hindlegs' have such short duration they are hardly heard

2.4 kHz →

CD1-31   **Semipalmated Plover** *Charadrius semipalmatus* Between Nome and Teller, Seward Peninsula, Alaska, USA, 10:46, 4 June 2004. Calls of 'flight call' type; an adult recorded near a nest with eggs, first standing its ground, then taking off. Background: Long-tailed Jaeger *Stercorarius longicaudatus*. 04.015.AB.01950.10

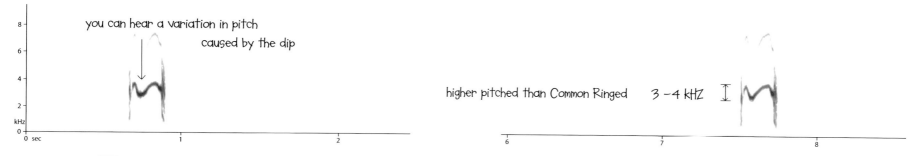

you can hear a variation in pitch caused by the dip

higher pitched than Common Ringed   3 – 4 kHz

Semipalmated Plover *Charadrius semipalmatus*, adult female, between Nome and Teller, Seward Peninsula, Alaska, USA, 4 June 2004 *(René Pop)*. Same bird as on CD1-31.

Separating stonechats by inflection

European Stonechat *S rubicola* has a variety of calls, and the most common are a *chat*, often compared to the sound of two stones being tapped together, and a whistled *weet* with an upward inflection (**CD1-32**). These are easy to see on a sonagram: the *chats* are vertical lines and the *weets* diagonal. The two are often given in alternation, with *chat* tending to take over from *weet* in the autumn. While in Kazakhstan, Magnus thought he noticed that the whistled sound in Siberian Stonechat had a downward inflection: *wiu* (**CD1-33**). The sonagram confirms the point nicely and the recordings support these observations. You can see the vertical trace produced by *chat* sounds interspersed with upward and downward inflected *weet* and *wiu* calls, respectively.

CD1-32   **European Stonechat** *Saxicola rubicola* North Hoy, Orkney, Scotland, 5 July 2001. *Weet* and *chat* calls of adult male, with more distant female. Background: Eurasian Curlew *Numenius arquata* and a colony of Common Gulls *Larus canus*. 01.030.MR.00433.00

Siberian Stonechat *Saxicola maurus* Steppes near Korgalzhyn, Aqmola Oblast, Kazakhstan, 25 May 2003. *Wiu* and *chat* calls of an adult male. Background: Common Quail *Coturnix coturnix*, White-winged Lark *Melanocorypha leucoptera*, Eurasian Skylark *Alauda arvensis*, Sykes's Blue-headed Wagtail *Motacilla flava beema* and Booted Warbler *Acrocephalus caligatus*. 03.021.MR.12120.11   **CD1-33**

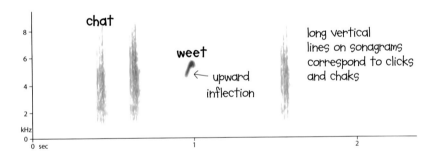

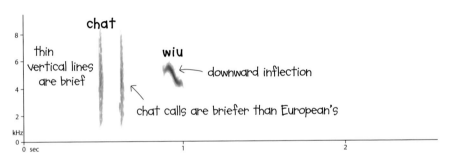

Rattles of Red-breasted Flycatchers

Rattles show in sonagrams as a series of the vertical *chat* or *tick* traces you've just learnt. These three sonagrams show the differences between rattling calls of Winter Wren *Troglodytes troglodytes*, Red-breasted Flycatcher *Ficedula parva* and Taiga Flycatcher *F albicilla*. In Red-breasted Flycatcher (**CD1-34**), the individual ticks are very evenly spaced; in Winter Wren (**CD1-35**), the ticks are not evenly spaced, but closer together at the start of each rattle. The flycatcher's rattle is also slower, in other words its ticks are spaced further apart. We can also use sonagrams to separate Red-breasted from Taiga Flycatcher (**CD1-36**), its recently split counterpart breeding from the Urals eastwards and occurring as a vagrant in Europe. In both flycatchers, the rattle is of roughly similar length, but in Taiga it contains many more ticks with much shorter gaps between them, and it slows down slightly towards the end. The resulting rattle is so different from that of Red-breasted that, as you can see in the sonagrams, Winter Wren fits in between.

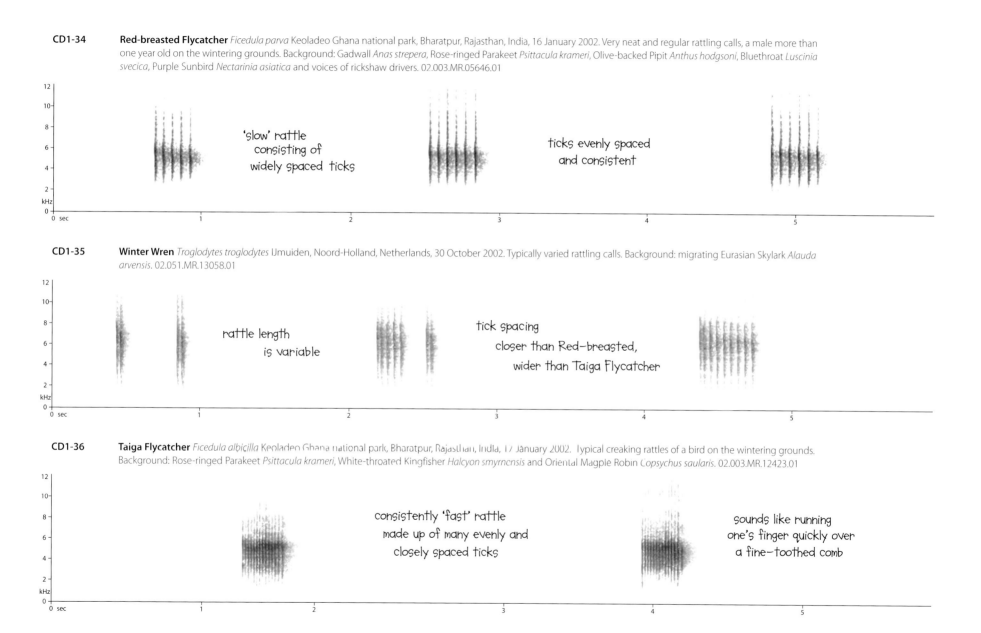

CD1-34 **Red-breasted Flycatcher** *Ficedula parva* Keoladeo Ghana national park, Bharatpur, Rajasthan, India, 16 January 2002. Very neat and regular rattling calls, a male more than one year old on the wintering grounds. Background: Gadwall *Anas strepera*, Rose-ringed Parakeet *Psittacula krameri*, Olive-backed Pipit *Anthus hodgsoni*, Bluethroat *Luscinia svecica*, Purple Sunbird *Nectarinia asiatica* and voices of rickshaw drivers. 02.003.MR.05646.01

'slow' rattle consisting of widely spaced ticks

ticks evenly spaced and consistent

CD1-35 **Winter Wren** *Troglodytes troglodytes* IJmuiden, Noord-Holland, Netherlands, 30 October 2002. Typically varied rattling calls. Background: migrating Eurasian Skylark *Alauda arvensis*. 02.051.MR.13058.01

rattle length is variable

tick spacing closer than Red-breasted, wider than Taiga Flycatcher

CD1-36 **Taiga Flycatcher** *Ficedula albicilla* Keoladeo Ghana national park, Bharatpur, Rajasthan, India, 17 January 2002. Typical creaking rattles of a bird on the wintering grounds. Background: Rose-ringed Parakeet *Psittacula krameri*, White-throated Kingfisher *Halcyon smyrnensis* and Oriental Magpie Robin *Copsychus saularis*. 02.003.MR.12423.01

consistently 'fast' rattle made up of many evenly and closely spaced ticks

sounds like running one's finger quickly over a fine-toothed comb

Gull long calls

Gull sounds are always with us, at least in western Europe, and for me living by the sea they can change a rather boring meeting into something quite bearable. Male and female Herring Gulls *Larus argentatus* stand on the roof opposite my office in Poole, Dorset, and pass opinion on every bird flying overhead. The most helpful sound to listen for is the long call, effectively the song of a gull. It can be heard at any time of the year, but particularly from adults and near-adults in late winter and during the breeding season. This one was recorded in March at a quiet spot in the Netherlands (CD1-37). These sonagrams are more complex than any you have tried so far. Cut them into pieces and they are much easier to understand. There are three separate stages to the long call, each with the gull adopting a different stance, and I hope that visualising these will help when reading the sonagrams. First, there are a few fairly low, short notes as the bird stretches its head a little forward. Then some longer, comparatively high-pitched notes are produced with the head pointing downwards. Finally the head is jerked upwards (in Herring Gull around 45° above the horizontal) and a long, loud series of fairly short, trumpeting notes are belted out.

In April 2003, Jacek Betleja took a group of us with him as he checked the breeding colony of Caspian Gulls *L cachinnans* at Babice in southern Poland (CD1-38). Having criticised field guide authors earlier on for their use of adjectives, I am going to have a go at describing something most of them ignore: Caspian Gull sounds. Caspian is the tenor to Herring Gull's alto and as you can see in the sonagram Caspian's long calls have the same three stages but the notes are deeper and richer in harmonics. After a few introductory calls, the long screamed notes of the second

Jacek Betleja and Bruce Mactavish ringing an adult Caspian Gull *Larus cachinnans* at breeding colony, Babice, Jankowice, Chrzanow, Poland, 25 April 2003 *(Arnoud B van den Berg)*

part sound as if it is straining for the Herring Gull's higher pitch while bowing much deeper. Next, the head is thrown all the way up to the vertical as it 'laughs' (*cachinnans* means 'laughing'). After the screamed middle, this diabolical cackling adds to the call's grotesque character. This is because of the speed of the notes, which you can compare with sonagrams of Herring and Yellow-legged Gulls *L michahellis*. Unlike both, a standing Caspian often opens its wings in an albatross-like posture while performing the long call. The recording was an adult giving two long calls while flying over its breeding colony. Long calls sound the same whether they are given in flight or on the ground.

Apart from cheering up a dull meeting, another reason for listening to the gulls at work is that there is always a chance that I'll hear a Yellow-legged Gull, as Poole is its only British breeding site. In summer we get a good influx here; the local pie factory and surroundings are home to over a hundred, and they substantially outnumber Lesser Black-backed Gulls *L fuscus*. Yellow-legged **(CD1-39)** has a long call that is uniformly deeper than that of Caspian Gull, with softer introductory notes and a far slower delivery, replacing all the maniacal qualities with sounds delivered at a pace you would expect from a bird that sits around eating pies all summer. The long call gestures are similar to Caspian but less exaggerated. Again, the sonagram gives you an impression of the speed of delivery. The length of long calls varies considerably in all gull species, while the speed of delivery and pitch do not.

Finally, here is a sonagram of a long call from a Lesser Black-backed Gull **(CD1-40)** for you to practice.

Caspian Gull *Larus cachinnans*, adult, Babice, Jankowice, Chrzanow, Poland, 25 April 2003 *(Arnoud B van den Berg)*. Regularly making the long call in flight while circling above its breeding colony on an islet along the Wisla river.

CD1-37   **Herring Gull** *Larus argentatus* Northern shore of Grevelingen, Zuid-Holland, Netherlands, 26 March 2003. Long call of an adult. Background: Mallard *Anas platyrhynchos*, other Herring Gulls and Dunnock *Prunella modularis*. 03.006.MR.15807.30

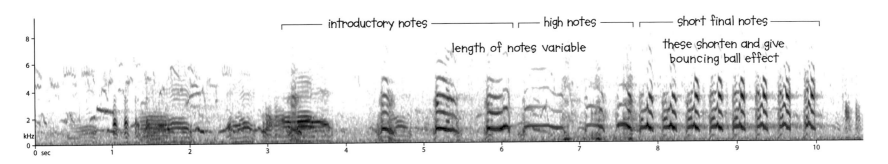

CD1-38   **Caspian Gull** *Larus cachinnans* Babice, Chrzanow, Poland, 14:52, 25 April 2003. Long calls in flight. Background: Black-headed Gull *L ridibundus*. 03.009.AB.02150.01

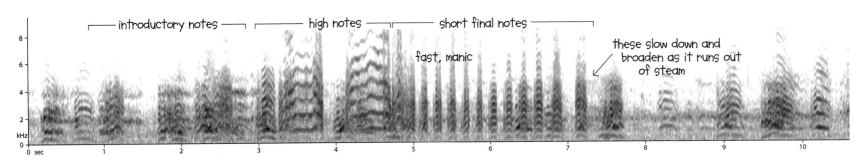

Yellow-legged Gull *Larus michahellis* Islote de Benidorm, País Valenciano, Spain, 7 August 2002. Long calls of a flock, mainly adults, socialising in flight before going to roost. 02.037.MR.14101.01

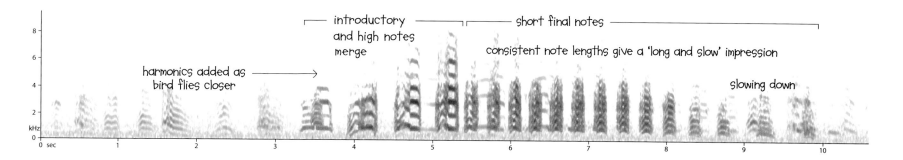

Lesser Black-backed Gull *Larus fuscus* IJmuiden, Noord-Holland, Netherlands, 10:18, 25 August 2000. A pair with one offspring flying past: long calls of an adult, *kow* calls of the other and whistled begging calls of the juvenile. 00.045.MR.00000.01

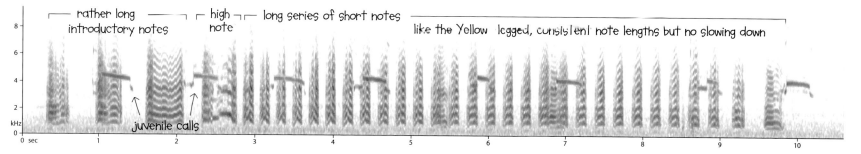

Loudness and intensity

The final measurement of bird sounds that we will consider is their loudness or quietness. In the same way that *pitch* relates to *frequency*, *loudness* is a word for how we perceive *intensity*, which is measured in decibels or dB. **How loud a sound seems depends not only on the effort put into making it, but also on its pitch, and the prevalent acoustics, including any other sounds audible at the same time.**

Loudness is shown in a sonagram by the depth of black in the tracing. When the sonagram is set to 'greyscale', a quiet whistle will show as a narrow, light grey line, whereas a loud one will be thicker and blacker. When judging loudness in a sonagram, it is wise to use the darkness of the tracing comparatively – and thus judge the louder parts of a song or call only in comparison with other parts of the same sonagram. A sonagram from another recording may not have been made from the same distance, or with the same equipment.

A helpful graph for illustrating loudness and timing is an oscillogram. It measures the sound waves. Their size above or below the horizontal axis tells us how loud the sound is. As usual, their change over time is read from left to right. Because a 1 kHz sound has 1000 waves per second, you have to zoom in a very long way to see that kind of detail. We don't need to see the individual waves; we can use oscillograms to see how the patterns of loudness change over time, and the rhythm or timing of the sounds.

Comparing woodpecker drums by oscillogram

Listen to typical drums of male Great Spotted Woodpecker *Dendrocopos major* (**CD1-41**) and male Lesser Spotted Woodpecker *D minor* (**CD1-42**). Compare what you hear: the differences in duration, the way loudness changes or stays the same over the course of the drum (the *envelope*), and the strike-rate in the individual drums. Now check these elements against the oscillogram. An additional difference not visible on these oscillograms is the length of the pauses between drums, which is much longer in the Great Spotted.

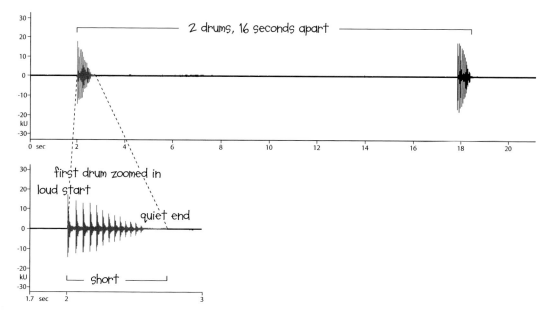

2 drums, 16 seconds apart

first drum zoomed in
loud start
quiet end
short

Great Spotted Woodpecker *Dendrocopos major* Biebrza marshes, Podłaskie, Poland, 07:21, 22 April 2003. Drumming of a male. Background: Common Wood Pigeon *Columba palumbus*, Common Chiffchaff *Phylloscopus collybita*, European Blue Tit *Cyanistes caeruleus* and Common Chaffinch *Fringilla coelebs*. 03.008.AB.05644.00

CD1-41

CD1-42   **Lesser Spotted Woodpecker** *Dendrocopos minor* Biebrza marshes, Podłaskie, Poland, 18:30, 1 May 2005. Drumming of a male. Background: Blackcap *Sylvia atricapilla*, Wood Warbler *Phylloscopus sibilatrix*, Common Chiffchaff *P collybita*, European Blue Tit *Cyanistes caeruleus*, Great Tit *Parus major* and Common Chaffinch *Fringilla coelebs*. 05.005.MR.14339.01

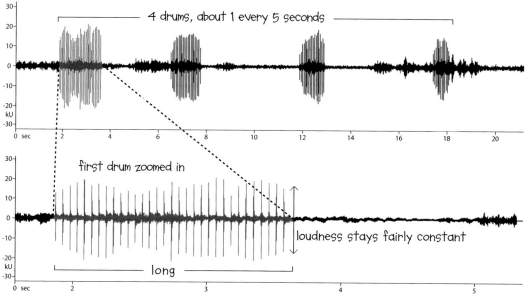

4 drums, about 1 every 5 seconds

first drum zoomed in
loudness stays fairly constant
long

45

Baillon's Crakes' emotions

Birds produce strong and weak sounds depending on the distance their message is intended to travel and the meaning they want to convey. Most birds produce weak, short-distance sounds when subsinging, copulating or comforting young, for example. Stronger, long-distance sounds are used to advertise for a mate, defend territory, contact others or mob a predator. Emotion always plays a part in this and many bird sounds increase in strength and change pitch depending on the emotional state. Listen to the recording of an adult Baillon's Crake *Porzana pusilla* (**CD1-43**), leading its young along a ditch. The continuously repeated weak *tuc… tuc… tuc…* calls it uses to keep the brood together gradually morph into louder (from 0:31) *tak!* calls as it senses danger (in this case the danger was Magnus). These louder calls are presumably not only intended for its young less than a metre away, but also for its mate about 10 m further along the ditch.

Baillon's Crake *Porzana pusilla*, Polder Achteraf, Noord-Holland, Netherlands, 18 August 2005 *(Phil Koken)*. One bird of the pair with young on CD1-43.

The power of a Thrush Nightingale

How loud a given sound seems to be depends on the acoustic conditions and the distance from the bird, as well as the direction the bird is facing. Describe each sound separately, and try to avoid unqualified use of the words 'loud' and 'soft'. *Powerful, moderate* and *weak* are more meaningful words to describe the power at which sound is produced. A flock of Greater Canada Geese *Branta canadensis*, with their low-pitched calls, flying over a house at dawn could wake the inhabitants, whereas the loud, high-pitched calls of a large flock of Redwings

T iliacus would not, even if they were much closer. The calls of both species in flight can be described as loud, but only Greater Canada calls can be described as powerful. Listen to this Thrush Nightingale *Luscinia luscinia* as it sings from a small island in a pond in the town park of Białowieza, Poland (**CD1-44**). The power of the song dominates over even closer songs of Eurasian Wryneck *Jynx torquilla*, Common Wood Pigeon *C palumbus*, Eurasian Collared Dove *Streptopelia decaocto*, Great Reed Warbler *A arundinaceus* and Common Chaffinch *Fringilla coelebs*. It held my attention so well I didn't notice the Icterine Warbler *Hippolais icterina* song that you can hear in the recording.

CD1-44   **Thrush Nightingale** *Luscinia luscinia* Białowieza village, Podlaskie, Poland, 05:44, 3 May 2005. Song; ambient recording with dawn chorus. Background: Common Sandpiper *Actitis hypoleucos*, Eurasian Collared Dove *Streptopelia decaocto*, Eurasian Wryneck *Jynx torquilla*, Great Reed Warbler *Acrocephalus arundinaceus*, Icterine Warbler *Hippolais icterina*, Common Chaffinch *Fringilla coelebs* and European Greenfinch *Chloris chloris*. 05.007.MC.11241.01

It is also worth noting that sounds learnt from published tapes and CDs can often give the wrong impression regarding the loudness of the sound; the birds invariably seem weaker when heard in the field. Previous bird sound publications have often been 'mastered' by people who did not have any field experience of the sounds, and set them all to play at the same volume.

Part 3: Bird recording in an acoustic slum

Acoustics and why bird recordings can sound different from real birds

I never wanted to be a sound recordist. I started in order to try and capture the bird sounds as they sounded to me in the field. I bought a microphone called a SASS or Stereo Ambient Sampling System, and mounted it next to my telescope in an effort to correctly identify, age and sex what was recorded. This I humped around the world staring through my scope and concentrating on bird identification while making recordings of different birds interspersed with jets, tractors, generators, peacocks, car tyres, dogs barking, my own breathing and other birders farting. Once The Sound Approach project started, my recordings made the others shudder. They didn't doubt the authentic 'birders ear' perspective but complained about all this background sound, the quality of the mics, and was that someone farting?

Arnoud and Magnus preferred using a mic set-up that gives you something closer to a 'bird's ear' perspective, mostly excellent all-purpose Telinga microphones, complete with transparent parabolic dish. These are made by Klas Strandberg, a microphone builder of great skill, living in the forests near Tobo in the middle of Sweden. With their lightweight construction,

Mark Constantine recording sounds with a Stereo Ambient Sampling System mounted next to his telescope, at back Anthony McGeehan and further up the trail Bruce Mactavish, High Point, New Jersey, USA, 8 May 1993 (Arnoud B van den Berg)

Magnus Robb and Maarten Pieter Lantsheer (right) using a Telinga microphone with transparent parabolic dish while recording migrating passerines, Kennemermeer, IJmuiden, Noord-Holland, Netherlands, 18 October 2005 (Arnoud B van den Berg)

Steep slopes of mount Kuro, habitat of Caucasian Snowcock *Tetraogallus caucasicus*, seen from mount Kazbeg, above Kazbegi, Kevi, Georgia, 23 June 2005 (René Pop). Inset: Caucasian Snowcock *Tetraogallus caucasicus*, Kazbegi, Kevi, Georgia, May 2004 (Kris De Rouck)

they are popular among bird recordists everywhere, and the dish can be rolled up for travel. They are also used by spies, and this has lead to some misunderstandings in sensitive spots around the world.

As you have read, low frequencies travel further than high ones, so a recording from further away - from a 'birder's ear' perspective - will tend to contain fewer high frequencies and sound somewhat less distinct. A closer recording - from a 'bird's ear' perspective - will contain more high frequencies, sounding crisper and clearer. Besides distance from the bird, the choice of microphone can also make a bird in a recording sound closer or more distant. The 'bird's ear' perspective of the Telinga is due to this mic amplifying high frequencies somewhat more than low ones, effectively bringing a bird closer. This is great news for a recordist, who can make high quality recordings of birds from a distance, their volume raised well clear of background sounds, while causing the birds a minimum of disturbance.

Gradually over the years we have reached a compromise. Holes were drilled in the casing of my beloved SASS, and the original hissy mics replaced with a high-powered pair of top-notch Sennheiser MKH-20s, a set-up pioneered by Lang Elliott. It's still mounted on a tripod, but with at least 10 m of cable between the recordist and the mics. I also bought and got the hang of the Telinga. Since using it I've come to realise that my high frequency hearing has always been poor. Wonderfully, it has enabled me to enjoy some high-pitched elements to bird sounds I'm sure I never heard before.

Both techniques have their advantages, and are at the two extreme ends of the types of mic used by bird sound recordists. The following examples illustrate the differences.

Degradation and Blackbird songs

First listen to a Common Blackbird recorded with a Telinga microphone at a moderate distance in a resonant Polish forest (CD1-45). Thanks to the parabolic dish, the sound is crisp and clear as if it had been recorded from much closer than it really was (50 m). Each song starts with the normal slower, mellow whistled part, which climbs and is followed by a faster, fine, higher-pitched series of notes at the end. This high frequency flourish has been emphasised by the Telinga mic. Then listen to the same bird recorded with the SASS from a similar distance (CD1-46). This is more of a birder's ear perspective, or indeed what a neighbouring blackbird might hear. In the SASS recording, the mellow whistling at the start of each song carries much more clearly than the flourish at the end. The flourish is more easily *degraded* by the blurring effects of the forest acoustic, not only because the SASS doesn't emphasise high sounds, but also because higher, shorter notes are much more easily absorbed and reflected by foliage and branches. The lower, longer notes of the mellow, whistled first part penetrate the forest better, and are not so easily degraded. As we will see later, degradation of sounds plays a very important role in the social relations of birds.

CD1-45 **Common Blackbird** *Turdus merula* Kuligi, Biebrza valley, Podłaskie, Poland, 10:02, 10 May 2005. Recording of singing adult male, made with a Telinga Pro V stereo parabolic microphone. Background: Blackcap *Sylvia atricapilla*, Common Chiffchaff *Phylloscopus collybita* and European Blue Tit *Cyanistes caeruleus*. 05.009.MR.10533.01

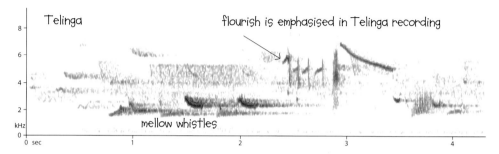

CD1-46 **Common Blackbird** *Turdus merula* Kuligi, Biebrza valley, Podłaskie, Poland, 10:25, 10 May 2005. Recording of singing adult male, made at the same location a few minutes later as previous track, using a Crown SASS fitted with Sennheiser MKH-20 omnidirectional stereo microphones. Background. Blackcap *Sylvia atricapilla*, Common Chiffchaff *Phylloscopus collybita*, Willow Warbler *P. trochilus*, Northern Bullfinch *Pyrrhula pyrrhula pyrrhula* and Yellowhammer *Emberiza citrinella*. 05.009.MR12143.11

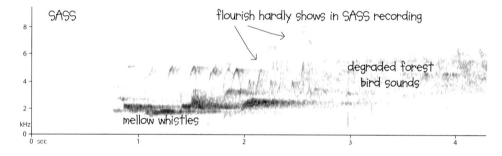

Woodcock roding and mics

Sometimes a parabolic microphone's emphasis on higher frequencies can go beyond simply bringing a bird closer, and it changes the picture. A good recordist using a parabolic microphone like the Telinga can compensate for this by pointing slightly away from the bird, or by altering the distance till the bird sounds more natural. But there are some cases where even these techniques are not enough. The 'roding' sound of a Eurasian Woodcock *Scolopax rusticola*, as it patrols over its territory at dusk, is a case in point. Roding combines two very different kinds of sound. Every three seconds or so, a series of deep grunts is followed by a very high-pitched squeak. The frequency of the grunts lies between about 0.6 and 1.5 kHz, perhaps not as deep as it seems, but much lower than the squeaks, which go from about 3 kHz to an amazing 14 kHz and back again in a 10th of a second! Pointing with a parabolic microphone, it is impossible to get the balance right between grunts and squeaks: inevitably the squeaks sound far too loud in the recording. Compare a recording made using a parabolic microphone **(CD1-47)** with a recording made using the SASS **(CD1-48)**. With the SASS, not only does the balance of grunt and squeak sound more natural, at least from a 'birder's ear' perspective, but the three-dimensional movement of the bird is also apparent to the listener, especially when using earphones.

Recording with a stereo Telinga, the temptation is to swing the dish round and follow the bird, which stays more or less in the middle of the stereo picture. With a SASS you hear the total environment and so the beautiful reverberation of the European Nightjar *Caprimulgus europaeus* in the SASS recording also demonstrates another advantage of an omnidirectional microphone. It captures echoes and reflections from the sides as well as the signal coming straight from the bird, giving a more realistic picture of environmental acoustics.

CD1-47   **Eurasian Woodcock** *Scolopax rusticola* Big Almaty lake, Almaty, Kazakhstan, 21:40, 30 May 2003. Roding display at dusk over semi-open Tien Shan Spruce *Picea schrenkiana* forest. 03.023.AB.01206.01

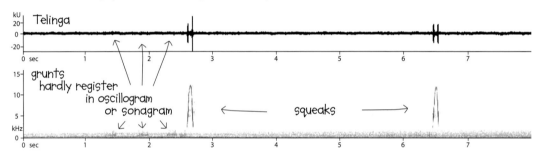

CD1-48   **Eurasian Woodcock** *Scolopax rusticola* and **European Nightjar** *Caprimulgus europaeus* Białowieza forest, Podłaskie, Poland, 22:00, 19 June 2005. Roding display of a woodcock, and churring song of a nightjar in semi-open pine forest. 05.017.MR.05950.01

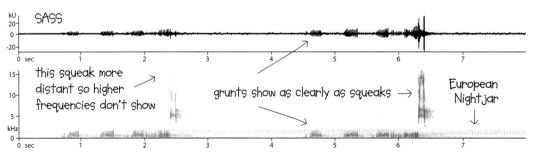

So if they give more realistic-sounding recordings, why don't we always use omnidirectional microphones like the SASS? The reason is that most of us live in an acoustic slum and very few places in Europe are as quiet as Białowieza forest and wind, planes, traffic and other low-frequency sounds get in the way of the bird. Ludwig Koch is considered to be one of the first bird sound recordists and reading his biography *Memoirs of a birdman* (1956) it was reassuring to hear him complain about background noise. In 1940 he was the first nature recordist to describe what has since become familiar: "We were just about to record this badly wanted 'noise' (the first ever recording of a bittern's boom) when a squadron of fighter-bombers roared overhead and as they chose to circle round and round over 'our studio' all further efforts were useless… I was able to hear such longed for notes as the grunting of the Water Rail and Lapwings and Redshanks performing quite close to my microphone. It was quite tantalising not to be able to pick up those calls." His *Encyclopedia of British birds* (1957), again a first, is one of my treasures as it has little known facts about bird sound in it. For example it was the first place I read of magpies having a "soft musical song which carries only ten or twenty yards" and as soon as I read about it I desperately wanted to hear it. Not knowing the sound, it was a bit of a surprise when I realised that they sang in my garden for weeks on end. This Eurasian Magpie *Pica pica* was recorded in Italy but sounds just like the chaps in my garden (**CD1-49**).

CD1-49   **Eurasian Magpie** *Pica pica* San Giovanni D'Asso, Toscana, Italy, 6 February 2003. Song. Background: Firecrest *Regulus ignicapilla* and European Blue Tit *Cyanistes caeruleus*. 03.001.MR.13329.12

Sometimes in July when Arnoud watches the Tour de France on his television he notices that each time the cyclists passed through a French countryside there were nightingales singing. He knows France well and he's sure Common Nightingale *L megarhynchos* stops singing around the 15th of June. So this would suggest that the TV sound engineers have done a little judicious engineering to brighten up this French countryside for their Dutch fans. Sound engineering is used in bird sound publications too. At its simplest it is a little filtering to remove low pitched sounds like distant engine noise. Next would come the removal of clicks, bumps and an annoying airplane sound half way through. A good example of this type of editing is the original recording I made of a Ural Owl *Strix uralensis* for CD1-02b, this recording being one of my first for the project. It was made in deep snow in bitterly cold weather, and days were spent in editing out the sounds of Dick, Killian, Pekka Pouttu and I shuffling in the snow to keep warm. This year we managed to replace it with a better recording and now you have a practically unaltered recording on this CD.

The Ural Owl is a good example because it has long gaps and on poor commercial CDs long gaps are often edited (shortened) to save space and keep the listeners' interest. Sometimes sounds are looped so that, to make a poor recording of a song work, the same phrase is repeated with suitable gaps. Very occasionally bird sounds are recreated when there has been no known recording and the bird has become extinct or extremely rare. An example can be found for Slender-billed Curlew *N tenuirostris* in Morocco on the CD series on African bird sounds by Claude Chappuis (2000).

Scenes are often created where the publication wants to convey a more wonderful scene than was captured. These normally include commentary and typically wish to show for example a Dartford Warbler *S undata* alarming at a Hobby *Falco subbuteo* which calls while a Wood Lark *Lullula arborea* sings in the background. For examples, see the publications by Geoff Sample (1996). We don't indulge in much of this… well only once so far. Listen again to the Black-eared Kite calls. Notice the Steller's Sea Eagle calling in the background? We edited that into the recording. There were Steller's calling in the vicinity but not in that recording so, just as an example (not to grip the listener you understand), we slipped it in.

Bird sound recordists are a suspicious lot and the final kind of editing may not even happen in real life. It is rumoured that this happens when a collection is being compiled and the authors don't have a complete set. Then perhaps for completeness another sound recordist's material is used without permission and edited in an attempt to avoid detection. Those collections where the date, place and recordist are not individually acknowledged are suspected of this.

In The Sound Approach, editing is minimalised. To let you know how, when and how much we have edited a sound we have devised a numbering sequence for each recording. The unique catalogue numbers at the bottom of each track listing refer to the year, the number of the tape for that year, the recordist's initials (AB for Arnoud van den Berg, DF for Dick Forsman, KM for Killian Mullarney, MC for Mark Constantine, MR for Magnus Robb), the place on the tape and finally the amount of editing, nought meaning no editing and three significantly edited. And the final number is the amount of filtering again from nought to three.

Forget the bird, listen to the scenery

Fifteen years ago I was fortunate enough to be sitting on a hotel veranda in Key Largo, Florida, USA. It was early in the morning and a Grey Plover (cf CD1-01a) called as it flew over the still water, beautifully audible at 500 m. Later, in the heat of the day, the same bird called as it flew at about the same distance over mudflats, and I could hardly hear it at all. This was because the warm afternoon air rising from the mud had muffled the sound, while in the morning the cold air and calm water had carried it.

A cool, still night is perfect for carrying sound and also for concentrating the mind on listening: owls and other nocturnal birds vocalise much less on rainy or windy nights. Night sounds can carry even further across the surface of a calm, cold lake. Listen to the Great Northern Loon *Gavia immer* recorded in perfect conditions in the twilight an hour after midnight at Myvatn, Iceland. It had been sleeping close to the shore, and when Magnus crept up for a closer look, the loon woke up and it gave this beautiful series of wails **(CD1-50)**.

Sounds recorded with the SASS, like all the recordings in this section, are perfect for gauging how the prevalent acoustics affects the way a bird sounds. Not only distance, but also temperature, wind, vegetation and topographical features can change a sound by the time it reaches our ears. Listen to the wails of the Great Northern Loon, each of which is answered by a faint echo slightly to the left, 2.8 seconds after the original wail (by listening carefully you can hear these at 0:04, 0:30, and 0:49). Just for fun, given that the speed of sound would have been about 333 m/sec (at around 3°C), the rock reflecting the echo must have been about 466 m away. This means that the sound

CD1-50   **Great Northern Loon** *Gavia immer* Myvatn, Iceland, 01:00, 24 June 2003. Wails of a paired adult.
Background: Long-tailed Duck *Clangula hyemalis*, European Golden Plover *Pluvialis apricaria* and Arctic
Tern *Sterna paradisaea*. 03.031.MR.03946.01

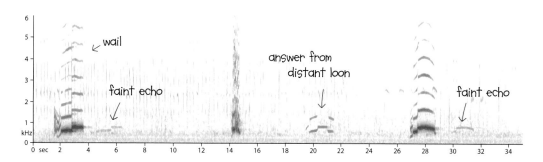

has travelled just under a kilometre by the time we hear the echo. More fun? Listen again and see if you can also hear an answer (0:20), which is not an echo, but came from another bird in a neighbouring territory further around the lake to the right.

If temperature and rising currents can affect the transmission of a sound, imagine what wind can do. For downwind listeners, a slight breeze can greatly improve the transmission of a sound. Meanwhile, upwind of the source much less is heard, and gusts of wind can obscure it completely. Rain or snowfall adds noise, and in poor weather most birds will save their energy; for others, like Rock Ptarmigan *Lagopus muta*, such conditions are normal. When male Rock Ptarmigans perform display flights, they take off with a call that has the rhythm of the famous wedding march

HERE comes the bride. Then, after they have flown some distance, they land with *…Comes the Bride…dedededede….* A Rock Ptarmigan at close range can sound very different from one heard at a distance.

Writing about this is much easier than recording it. It was 02:00 am, and Killian and I were in a desolate part of northern Norway. He was away with the parabola, recording Eurasian Dotterel *C morinellus* courtship. After struggling through several flat batteries and loose cables in the freezing cold and snow, the wind buffeting my ears via the mics was finally too much for me. I picked up the equipment, threw it in the back of the car, wound up the windows and screamed obscenities. I now blush to think that Killian has a recording of this slight wobbly. Anyway, calm

CD1-51   **Rock Ptarmigan** *Lagopus muta* Tanner Bru, Finnmark, Norway, 02:00, 7 June 2003. Flight display of male. Background: snow shower. 03.024.MC.02320.31 & 03.024.MC.05415.31

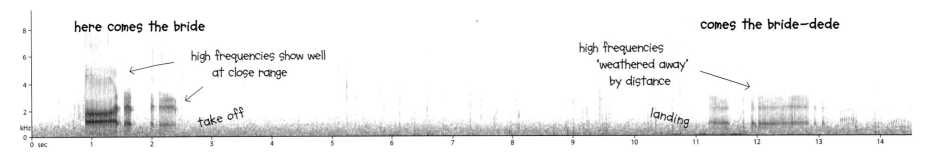

returned and at 03:00 am I made a series of recordings. They still weren't quite right, and we have edited the start of one recording to the end of another. However, I promise this is exactly as it sounded in real life. So listen now to the single performance as the bird sings and flies over 100 m away and sings again. You can hear the snow on the mics and how both distance and the snow shower 'weather' away the higher frequencies of the call given on landing **(CD1-51)**. The timbre as it lands in the distance is really quite different, a much more rounded, less dry sound, whereas in reality the bird is producing a more or less identical timbre both on taking off and landing.

In some cases, low parts of the sound can be the first to disappear at a distance. It depends on how powerfully the different frequencies are produced at the source, and also on other sounds in the environment, which may have a masking effect. Thanks to Marek Borkowski, who maintains large parts of the famous Biebrza marshes in Poland for conservation, we were able to make recordings of displaying Great Snipe *Gallinago media*. First, a stunning 'bird's ear' recording of male Great Snipe making some amazing popping and whizzing sounds as they defend their patch at a traditional, communal display site or 'lek' **(CD1-52)**. At close range, a deep and rather quiet *tup-tup-tup…* which Marek calls the 'tractor' sound can be heard, along with the sound made by their wings as they leap in display.

Now listen to a full atmospheric recording that I made two years earlier **(CD1-53)**. Under a sky completely full of the 'drumming' sounds of displaying Common Snipe *G gallinago*, a Great Snipe lek can just be heard. At a distance of about 60 m, which puts it firmly in the 'birder's ear' category, only the high frequency popping sounds carry well. Besides the effects of distance, there is also competition from louder, closer sounds at similar frequencies: the throbbing wings of a displaying Northern Lapwing *Vanellus vanellus*, and the little barking sounds of Moorfrogs *Rana arvalis*.

CD1-52   **Great Snipe** *Gallinago media* Biebrza marshes, Podlaskie, Poland, 23:35, 14 May 2005. Several males at a traditional lek. Background: Spotted Crake *Porzana porzana*, Corn Crake *Crex crex*, Bluethroat *Luscinia svecica*, Aquatic Warbler *Acrocephalus paludicola*, Great Reed Warbler *A arundinaceus* and European Tree Frog *Hyla arborea*. 05.012.MR.11413.00

CD1-53 Common Snipe *Gallinago gallinago* and **Great Snipe** *G media* Biebrza marshes, Podłaskie, Poland, 20:10, 20 April 2003. Aerial drumming displays of Common Snipe, with a distant Great Snipe lek (it can be heard at 0:02 – 0:07, 0:35 – 0:41 and 1:11 – 1:17). Background: Great Bittern *Botaurus stellaris*, Northern Lapwing *Vanellus vanellus* and Moorfrog *Rana arvalis*. 03.009.MC.02800.01

Over a couple of years the three of us spent hours along the 'Bison's Ribs' trail in the Białowieza forest in Poland, recording woodpeckers. It's a magical place and you get the distinct feeling that forest gods are somehow in charge of proceedings. Each of us has his own style. Arnoud is the first out, hungrily prowling round with his parabola, arm outstretched, boots deep in the water, striding out for miles hunting down his target species. Magnus has an ill-deserved reputation for lying in, then needing two cups of coffee before he can function, then he also goes into prowl mode and will stay up all night at the drop of a hat. My own style is sedentary, I carry the SASS and cables in a wicker basket to a quiet spot, unfold my stool, sit down and sink into reverie as I wait for something to turn up.

On the first visit, I recorded many woodpeckers drumming, and desperately wanted them to be the ever elusive White-backed Woodpecker *D leucotos*, but each time Arnoud returned from his travels he would tell me that he had only seen Great-spotted

White-backed Woodpecker *Dendrocopos leucotos*, Białowieza, Podłaskie, Poland, 1 May 2003 (*Arnoud B van den Berg*). Parent at nest 'found' by Mark.

Woodpeckers. After several days, Arnoud was back asleep in his van when the forest gods gave me a little gift. A tour bus full of birdwatchers arrived some way away but visible from where I was sitting in the woods. The leader then set his scope on a nest hole. Having seen what was peeping out I couldn't wait to get back to tell Arnoud, without bird bus detail, that I had at last found the White-backed's nest hole.

Competitive urges to make the ultimate recording are perfect for mischievous forest gods. Two years later as I lay-a-bed, Magnus,

out early, had at last found and recorded (with the Telinga) the elusive Three-toed Woodpecker *Picoides tridactylus* drumming several kilometres along Bison's Rib trail. He phoned me, I gathered my basket and SASS (perfect for this kind of recording), walked to his spot and settled down. Magnus returned for his breakfast, and while he was away, I made the following recordings (**CD1-54a**). I hope he has forgiven me.

As I said, the ancient forest ambience is mystical, almost sacred, but it all comes down to sound *degradation*. Fallen trees, grasses

CD1-54a
0:00 – 1:25

Three-toed Woodpecker *Picoides tridactylus* Białowieza forest, Podłaskie, Poland, 09:30, 4 May 2005. Drumming male at a distance. Background: Common Wood Pigeon *Columba palumbus*, Common Blackbird *Turdus merula*, Blackcap *Sylvia atricapilla*, Wood Warbler *Phylloscopus sibilatrix* and Common Chaffinch *Fringilla coelebs*. 05.008.MC.02045.01

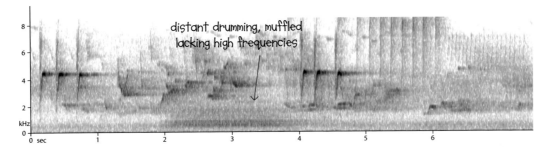

CD1-54b
1:27 – 2:20

Three-toed Woodpecker *Picoides tridactylus* Białowieza forest, Podłaskie, Poland, 09:33, 4 May 2005. Drumming male at very close range. Background: Common Cuckoo *Cuculus canorus*, Common Blackbird *Turdus merula*, Blackcap *Sylvia atricapilla*, Wood Warbler *Phylloscopus sibilatrix* and Common Chaffinch *Fringilla coelebs*. 05.008.MC.02410.01

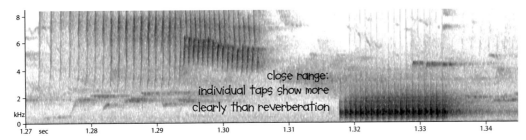

and more obviously the boughs, twigs and foliage of trees and bushes can block, absorb and reflect bird sounds. Listen to the drumming of this male Three-toed Woodpecker when he was still at a distance (**CD1-54a**). Don't turn up the volume: listen to it as part of the forest ambience, taking its place among Wood Warblers *P sibilatrix*, Common Chaffinches, and a host of other forest birds. Three minutes later *the* recording was made, the mics at exactly the same spot, when the male flew in and started drumming just above them (**CD1-54b**).

Listen to both examples again. In the more distant recording, the drumming sound reflects and echoes off hundreds of tree trunks and millions of spruce needles, twigs and sprouting alder leaves. Due to the varying distances travelled, the sound is arriving along each pathway at a slightly different time. It's more difficult to hear the individual taps, and they lack definition. You can clearly hear that the sound is degraded. Nearly everything you can hear of the drum in the more distant recording is reverberation; very little sound is coming directly from the source. In the second cut the drumming sound, besides being much louder, is now quite different in timbre. At this close range, most of the sound is coming straight to the mics, with only a little reverberation heard after each drum.

Acoustics change with the seasons, and the effects of vegetation growth and withering, prevailing weather conditions and the degree to which other species are also vocalising all have an effect. Birds may time their songs and displays to coincide with the most favourable acoustics. Woodpeckers do most of their drumming in the last couple of weeks before foliage appears. Three-toed Woodpecker, although we recorded it at this time, actually drums for a longer period, being an inhabitant of evergreen spruce forests.

How birds adapt to acoustics

I was in the northern forests of New Jersey, listening to the dawn chorus, when I first noticed that birds seem to take their turn to perform. An American Robin *T migratorius* first, then the stunningly beautiful song of a Veery *Catharus fuscescens*, followed by the Black-capped Chickadee *Poecile atricapilla*, Grey Catbirds *Dumetella carolinensis*, and then Baltimore Oriole *Icterus galbula* got started. By six o'clock, Chestnut-sided Warbler *Dendroica pensylvanica*, then at 06:15 Downy Woodpecker *P pubescens*, Hermit Thrush *C guttatus*, Yellow-throated Vireo *Vireo flavifrons* and on and on. It's the same in Europe although such a diverse forest avifauna is hard to come by. Birds are adept at taking advantage of good acoustics and, at dawn, the atmosphere is at its most suitable for carrying sounds, while wind and convection currents are at their weakest. While it is too dark to forage and predators are not yet up and about, birds like to check whether all the neighbouring territories are still occupied, and answering each other in song is a quick and efficient way to do this. Most species join the dawn chorus in a predictable order each day, linked primarily with light intensity. It is thought that they get a little earlier in relation to dawn until the peak of breeding and then the pattern reverses. Birds make less sound straight after dawn when they forage, then there is a little surge. Things decrease through the day as the acoustics deteriorate, and increase again in late afternoon as they improve.

A reed bed presents a formidable obstacle to bird sounds; the reed stems and leaves are a physical barrier, but they also rustle in the slightest breeze, masking many sounds. Despite this, the *booming* of Great Bittern (CD1-02a) is so powerful and deep that it can be heard several kilometres away. This type of low-frequency sound travels round and even through solid objects. For the tiny Cetti's Warbler *Cettia cetti* to be heard it has had to develop a tremendously powerful song in order to penetrate the reed beds. On the other hand, an Aquatic Warbler *A paludicola* has to use very different tactics if its weaker, higher-frequency song is to be heard from any distance. Waiting for ideal acoustics in the late afternoon or just before dusk, it perches on one of the highest stems in its sedge field habitat. Listen to this SASS recording, made at about 10-20 m, as it then makes a series of

Caspian Snowcock *Tetraogallus caspius*, male, Sivrikaya, Rize, Turkey, 12 May 1987 *(Arnoud B van den Berg)*. Singing.

CD1-55   **Aquatic Warbler** *Acrocephalus paludicola* Biebrza marshes, Podłaskie, Poland, 20:00, 10 May 2005. Song flights at dusk. Background: Great Bittern *Botaurus stellaris*, Common Crane *Grus grus*, Common Snipe *Gallinago gallinago*, Eurasian Woodcock *Scolopax rusticola* (0:24, distant: only the low grunts are audible), Common Cuckoo *Cuculus canorus*, Thrush Nightingale *Luscinia luscinia*, Common Blackbird *Turdus merula* and Common Grasshopper Warbler *Locustella naevia*. 05.010.MR.01830.01

song flights, crossing its territory from left to right during the peak of the evening chorus (**CD1-55**). In the distance (over 500 m), you can hear a Great Bittern booming, the reeds having degraded the sound so much that now it sounds like someone blowing over the mouth of a bottle. Some of the Common Cranes *Grus grus* trumpeting in the distance sound more like wind in the rigging of a boat as the distance distorts the sound.

In mountain habitats, the 'white noise' of fast moving streams can overpower many bird sounds, while rocks can reflect and distort the sounds. On the other hand, birds that sing in cliff and mountain habitats use features of the landscape to project their song to incredible distances. Urban singers do the same with buildings: think of a Common Blackbird or a Common Starling *Sturnus vulgaris* singing from a rooftop. A beautiful example is

Caspian Snowcock *Tetraogallus caspius* Demirkazık, Adana, Turkey, 06:00, 4 May 2001. Two birds singing from precipices along a circular ridge or cirque. Background: Alpine Accentor *Prunella collaris*, Black Redstart *Phoenicurus ochruros* and Red-billed Chough *Pyrrhocorax pyrrhocorax*. 01.016.MR.00041.01   **CD1-56**

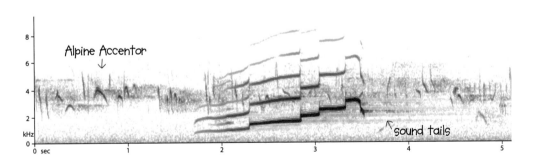

Caucasian Snowcock *Tetraogallus caucasicus*, Kazbegi, Kevi, Georgia, 23 June 2005 *(Arnoud B van den Berg)*. René Pop overlooking Kazbeg glacier; on the slopes to the right, Caucasian Snowcock was singing.

Caucasian Snowcock *Tetraogallus caucasicus*, Kazbegi, Kevi, Georgia, May 2003 *(Ruedi Aeschlimann)*

provided by this recording of Caspian Snowcocks *Tetraogallus caspius* **(CD1-56)**. Perched on top of a precipitous ridge in the Taurus mountains of southern Turkey, their songs carry over the rocks. These birds are singing in a natural amphitheatre several kilometres across. The sound reflects off several cliff faces, resonating beautifully and giving them all the more 'presence'

(note for example the echo of the more distant bird at 0:54). Caucasian Snowcock *T caucasicus* is very sought after, and this is the first available recording **(CD1-57)**. Arnoud and René Pop

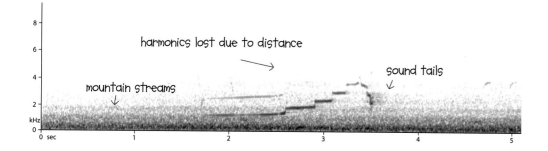

Caucasian Snowcock *Tetraogallus caucasicus* Kazbegi, Greater Caucasus, Georgia, 20:26, 21 June 2005. Whistled song by several individuals. Background: Water Pipit *Anthus spinoletta* and mountain streams. 05.013.AB.11223.11   **CD1-57**

climbed the 2600 m to the snow on the steep slopes of mount Kuro to record these birds at dusk. Caucasian prefer the edge of the snowline and have to compete with noisy streams full of melt snow. You can hear several birds calling above the mountain streams, and they pitch their calls at frequencies higher than most of this 'white' noise. René, so exhausted by the climb, slept and snored, yet his low pitch snoring cannot be heard above the stream in this recording.

When you look at a sonagram you can see the acoustics as well as the bird sound. For example, you can see a 'sound tail' after the notes as the sound echoes off of the surroundings.

One group of species that have to deal with a great variety of conditions is the larks Alaudidae. Listen to a recording of a sky absolutely full of Eurasian Skylarks *Alauda arvensis* over the vast steppes of Kazakhstan **(CD1-58)**. As you can hear in the recording, the next bird is not far away, so wind and currents won't damage the song too much at this kind of distance. In the stiff competition for a piece of the steppes to call their own, they have to sing with virtuosity and intricate detail.

CD1-58   **Eurasian Skylark** *Alauda arvensis* Karazhar, Aqmola Oblast, Kazakhstan, 23 May 2003. A chorus of skylarks over the steppes. Background: Greylag Goose *Anser anser*, Common Quail *Coturnix coturnix*, Eurasian Curlew *Numenius arquata* and Great Bittern *Botaurus stellaris*. 03.018.MR.04543.01

CD1-59   **Greater Hoopoe Lark** *Alaemon alaudipes* Merzouga, Tafilalt, Morocco, 09:52, 29 March 2002. Song in flight in a sand desert; the bird's wingbeats as it somersaults can be heard in the second and third songs. 02.006.AB.10918.21

Listen to a lone Greater Hoopoe Lark *Alaemon alaudipes* **(CD1-59)**, recorded in a huge desert of sand dunes in eastern Morocco. In this habitat, food resources are few and far between, and birds are spaced much further apart, at distances somewhere

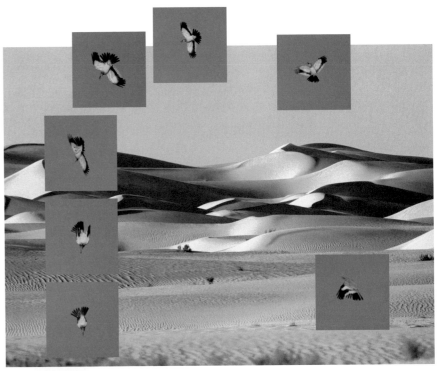

Greater Hoopoe Lark *Alaemon alaudipes*, male, Morocco, 1 April 2006 *(Arnoud B van den Berg)*. Singing while somersaulting in the air, flashing white in the wings.

between 500 m and a kilometre. To avoid the heat of the desert and its unfavourable effects on song this lark sings in the morning when the atmosphere is cooler and calmer. One of the great sights of the desert is when this lark delivers its song while leaping up from a bush or sandy knoll then, still singing, somersaults in the air, flashing the white of its wings. This song is far carrying, perhaps because of the force of delivery but mainly because its simplicity, which allows long distance transmission with a minimum of degradation.

The arctic tundra is a cold and windy place. During the short summer, food is not so scarce for the few that are tough enough to cope with the climate, and Horned Larks *Eremophila alpestris* are able to live at densities somewhere between the extremes of steppe and sand desert. Listen to one struggling against the wind as it sings over the north-eastern Siberian tundra **(CD1-60)**. Magnus recorded this while he was stranded during a six-day period of easterly gales, and he had to hold the parabolic microphone with both hands to stop it blowing away. Horned Larks are thought to take turns in song flights (Drury 1961) and the song period is short so they don't waste too much time in this fruitless pursuit. The bird's main weapon against the wind may simply be repetition. Like many Arctic birds, especially waders, Horned Lark works on the principle that if it repeats a relatively simple kind of song often enough, the message will get through, even if most renditions are obstructed by gusts of wind.

The Wood Lark has a pretty cushy life, at least as far as singing is concerned. It breeds at moderate densities, in comparatively calm, semi-open habitats where it rises in song flight giving this magical song. Often, as in the case of this recording, it will perch in a tree or on a post to deliver its song. I just set up the equipment under its favourite tree, moved away to sit under another almond tree and waited for the performance to start. To conclude this section, listen to this singer of the Spanish dehesas, with accompanying Eurasian Hoopoes *Upupa epops*, Iberian Azure-winged Magpies *Cyanopica cooki* and a host of other Extremaduran delights **(CD1-61)**. None of these other birds is using quite the same frequency range as the Wood Lark, so it has this acoustic niche all to itself.

Wood Lark *Lullula arborea* Torrejón El Rubio, Extremadura, Spain, 07:30, 11 May 2004. Song delivered from perch in a tree in the Spanish dehesas, a savannah-like habitat. Background: Common Quail *Coturnix coturnix*, Common Cuckoo *Cuculus canorus*, Eurasian Hoopoe *Upupa epops*, Iberian Azure-winged Magpie *Cyanopica cooki* and Rock Sparrow *Petronia petronia*. 04.012.MC.13823.12 **CD1-61**

CD1-60 **Horned Lark** *Eremophila alpestris* Lena delta, Yakutia, Russia, 22:30, 22 June 2004. Song in strong wind over the Arctic tundra. Background: Little Stint *Calidris minuta*. 04.032.MR.01953.01

Part 4: 'I bird with Bill Smith'

No bird has just one call or one song

As you can tell from the quotes and references in this guide I am a bird expert groupie. It's not all that I am, but it was the point made to me by my friend Steve Smith when for my birthday he gave me a T shirt with 'I bird with Steve Smith' printed on it. T shirts are a bit like an advert or label and I have to admit to never having worn it. Anyway I've now found a bird expert called Smith, although I've never met him. W J Smith isn't fond of labels either and he wrote a vigorous attack on the oversimplified labelling of bird calls in our field guides (Smith 1996) that has encouraged me to think twice before labelling a bird sound.

It seems reassuring and straightforward to label a sound as an alarm call, a flight call, territorial song and so on, but Smith emphasised that **birds use the same vocalisations for more than one purpose or strategy; one and the same *signal* can convey different *messages* depending on the *recipient*.** So when we are tempted to interpret the meaning of a sound, we need to be as broad-minded as we can.

It's easy to misinterpret or oversimplify a bird's behaviour and there is a great story that illustrates this point in *Mind of the raven* by Bernd Heinrich (2000), where the author tells of a man who was being chased by a Grizzly Bear *Ursus arctos horribilis*. As the man ran, a Common Raven *Corvus corax* guided him with its calls, and by following this bird he miraculously escaped the bear. On recounting the story to the author, a renowned expert on raven behaviour, the chap was shocked as it was explained to him that the raven was unlikely to be guiding him but rather calling the bear to the man so that it would kill him and enable the raven to feed off the scraps.

Looking at identification papers in most journals, or in field guides, the convention to name *the* song or *the* call is powerful and widespread. Yet read *The birds of the Western Palearctic* (BWP) or an original research paper and you may be amazed how many vocalisations can be attributed to a Common Blackbird or a House Sparrow *Passer domesticus* or indeed a Common Raven. The misconception that each bird has just one song and one call is only a slight advance on childhood, when we allowed them one sound each: all ducks said *quack* and all owls said *too-whit too-woo*. In its adult guise, this kind of thinking is responsible for much of what we seem to screen out. Near where I live in Dorset is the swannery at Abbotsbury. When I first heard the variety of sounds made by Mute Swans as they were being fed, I was really surprised. I thought they were supposed to be mute, and yet even these birds have a range of different vocal and hissing sounds, besides the wing sounds and grunting call we heard earlier (CD1-08). Slowly over the years I noticed Mute Swans calling everywhere. I don't know what species I had attributed these sounds to before. Common Moorhen *Gallinula chloropus*? Eurasian Coot *Fulica atra*? It's serendipity I suppose, as with so many subjects; the more you read and listen, the more variety you will discover.

Long-billed Dowitcher *Limnodromus scolopaceus*, first-winter, Veerse Meer, Zeeland, Netherlands, 3 January 2004 *(Marten van Dijl)*. Same bird as on CD1-66.

There can often be occasions when it is difficult to know where to draw the line between a 'song' and a 'call', and it is best not to be too rigid in making those distinctions. In early June 2002, I was in Finland listening to a Brambling *F montifringilla* (**CD1-62**), and as expected it was singing a flat buzzing note repeated every five seconds or so. Later that month, while sitting on the wall by the river outside my hotel in Gavarnie high in the French Pyrenees, I recorded a Common Chaffinch perched on top of a small tree making a similar but shorter sound and delivered faster (**CD1-63**). I started to think about Smith's warnings. This kind of sound is usually labelled as a call, and in fact a whole class of repetitive sounds made by chaffinches from prominent perches are known as 'rain calls'. In any given area, all birds will use the same note, and these sounds are traditionally considered to show regional dialects as they vary from location to location. Whatever sound is used, a buzz, a whistle or a more complex sound, it is always delivered at regular intervals.

Smith's attack went like this: "Field guides recognize as songs only the most widely accepted cases… Other vocalisations are listed, if at all, as nonsong 'calls'. The simpler vocalisations of many species are relegated to nonsong status even if often uttered in the sustained quasi-rhythmic bouts diagnostic of singing performances" (Smith 1996). Smith was talking of North American field guides but in fact most field guides, for brevity and convenience, have perpetuated the myth that birds have one song and one call, and rarely question what belongs in which category. Once you consider chaffinch 'rain calls' from Smith's perspective, you have to question whether they make more sense as songs.

Having read more on the subject, I now realise that my thoughts on rain calls were not original. Thielcke (1969) was of the opinion that the rain call was a kind of a "song substitute". The lack of a musical comparative chaffinch-like song in Brambling is intriguing, although if both taxa have two choices of song type it makes perfect sense for the taxa breeding in the colder north to drop the complex song and opt for an energy saving repeated call-song. So where does this leave us? How should these sounds be described: song or call? Draw your own conclusions as you listen to the Brambling and Common Chaffinch examples, then listen to a recording of a typical European Greenfinch *Chloris chloris*, which is also repeating a commonly heard Brambling-like sound in a song-like performance (**CD1-64**).

CD1-62   **Brambling** *Fringilla montifringilla* Inari, Lapland, Finland, 4 June 2002. Song of adult male. Background: Wood Sandpiper *Tringa glareola*, Willow Warbler *Phylloscopus trochilus*, Pied Flycatcher *Ficedula hypoleuca* and Common Reed Bunting *Emberiza schoeniclus*. 02.012.MC.02424.02

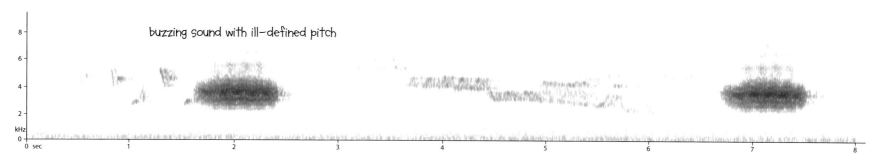

buzzing sound with ill-defined pitch

CD1-63   **Common Chaffinch** *Fringilla coelebs* Gavarnie, Hautes-Pyrénées, France, 16:00, 18 June 2002. Simple repeated buzzing song or 'rain call'. Background: Blackcap *Sylvia atricapilla* and mountain river. 02.016.MC.01901.23

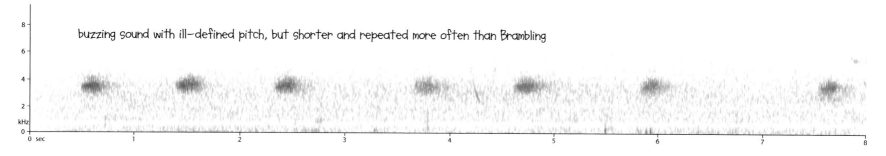

buzzing sound with ill-defined pitch, but shorter and repeated more often than Brambling

CD1-64   **European Greenfinch** *Chloris chloris* Akseki, Antalya, Turkey, 11 May 2001. Simple repeated buzzing song, recorded at 1400 m altitude in an ancient fir forest. Background: Ehrenberg's Redstart *Phoenicurus phoenicurus samamisicus*, Krüper's Nuthatch *Sitta krueperi*, Coal Tit *Periparus ater* and European Serin *Serinus serinus*. 01.018.MR.12015.10

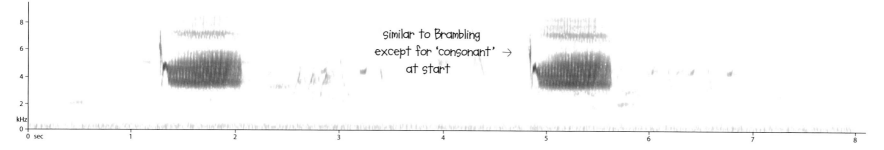

similar to Brambling
except for 'consonant' →
at start

Short-billed *Limnodromus griseus* and Long-billed Dowitchers *L scolopaceus* are a classic pair of birds in which sound clinches identification. Travelling in Texas with Anthony and Bruce, I spent a lot of time asking them to describe what they could hear when either species flushed. Bruce had very little experience with Long-billed, whereas for Anthony it was Short-billed that was less familiar. One time on San Padre Island we were discussing the finer details of separating them, when Anthony suggested flushing a small group of dowitchers just beyond a reedy fringe. Five alligators noisily broke cover in front of him. I listened to my tape of the event recently and "alligator infested" was all he said, then confirmed the identification as "Long-billed". When things calmed down we started to realise that the call they make when they take off is not the same as the one they use in steady flight. If you are ever lucky enough to find a dowitcher *Limnodromus* in Europe, you'll really need to hear 'the' call. Imagine the scene (as often as I have); looking round to make sure no one is watching you flush the bird, and fortunately it takes flight giving a short series of calls. Checking the American field guide you bought to keep in the pannier of your bike, just in case, you read "… **flight call** … Short-billed Dowitcher … a staccato trebled *tututu*; … Long-billed Dowitcher … a single thin *keek* occasionally doubled or trebled" (Peterson 1980). This was what happened to Irish birders in the sixties who heard dowitchers giving multiple-note calls as they took off and thought, reasonably, that they were hearing Short-billeds. Several were identified in this way. Now we are better informed on the matter of dowitcher vocalisations. We know that when Long-billed *take flight* they often give a rapid series of short notes, rather like Short-billed. The diagnostic high-pitched, single-note *keek* is used both on the ground and when the bird is in steady flight. The written descriptions of calls in accounts of the Irish dowitchers were excellent, enabling those reviewing the records in later years to correctly record the birds as Long-billed.

It's a strange aspect of a birder's psychology that having found a rare bird he returns to the same site over and over again in subsequent years partly paying homage to "The Sender" for the blessing and partly in the hope of seeing the bird again. On the last day of June 2004 Killian was doing just this. Having had unsatisfactory views of a distant Great Knot *Calidris tenuirostris* at the end of June 2000 he was looking again, as he had every year since, in all the suitable spots around Wexford, Ireland. As he scanned through large flocks of Black-tailed Godwits *Limosa limosa* and Common Redshanks *Tringa totanus* on Our Lady's Island Lake he picked up a dowitcher. Although it was summer the bird was in winter plumage. He videoed it and could see that the identification was not straightforward. Then it took off and flew straight over his head, but it didn't call. Frustrating because, as we have already shown, had it called that would have identified it. Killian returned home and that night, having gone through all the feather tracts by watching the video in detail, decided that it was a Short-billed Dowitcher and clarified the identification on the bird news services. He returned the next two days and on the second day it called, confirming his identification.

Now all he had to do was record it for us. He returned over and over again but the loudness of the redshanks drowned the dowitcher's calls and the conversational calls of the godwits sounded surprisingly similar. It was very frustrating and despite repeatedly sitting with the birds, Telinga poised and tape running, it took until the 20th of July to get it recorded. Even then, his recording had to be edited to remove an annoyingly close redshank call in order to create a less confusing recording (**CD1-65**). The Long-billed Dowitcher in **CD1-66** was also a vagrant, one that spent two winters in the Netherlands. This bird was nearly always found in the company of a Common Redshank. Fortunately, this time it was on its own, and it was recorded before flying back to join its friend. It would have been easier to use the recordings we have from North America but it's far more exciting to hear genuine vagrants.

Short-billed Dowitcher *Limnodromus griseus*, first-summer, Our Lady's Island Lake, Wexford, Ireland, 2 July 2004 *(Killian Mullarney)*. Same bird as on CD1-65.

CD1-65 **Short-billed Dowitcher** *Limnodromus griseus* Our Lady's Island Lake, Wexford, Ireland, 20 July 2004. Calls on taking off. Background: Dunlin *Calidris alpina* and Common Tern *Sterna hirundo*. 04.001.KM.15555.32

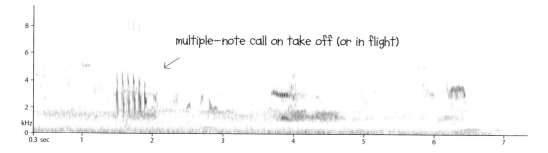

multiple-note call on take off (or in flight)

CD1-66 **Long-billed Dowitcher** *Limnodromus scolopaceus* Veerse Meer, Zeeland, Netherlands, 09:30, 7 January 2004. Multiple-note calls on taking off, then single note keek calls in flight. Background: Eurasian Wigeon *Anas penelope*, Eurasian Oystercatcher *Haematopus ostralegus*, Common Redshank *Tringa totanus* and distant tractor. 04.001.MR.02610.01

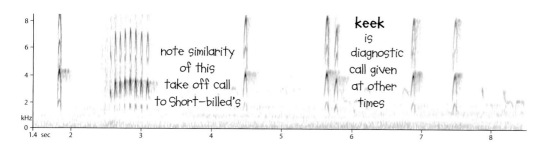

note similarity of this take off call to Short-billed's

keek is diagnostic call given at other times

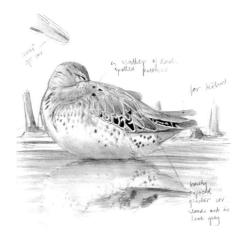

Short-billed Dowitcher *Limnodromus griseus*, first-summer, Our Lady's Island Lake, Wexford, Ireland, 11 July 2004 *(Killian Mullarney)*. Same bird as on CD1-65.

Cracking the code

The best way to take bird sound identification beyond '*the* call, *the* song' thinking is to start comparing broader repertoires. To get an idea of the repertoire of a given species, we normally start with BWP, the only publication that really gives enough detail apart from the German *Stimmen der Vögel Europas* by Bergmann & Helb (1982). Most closely related species will have parallel call or song types for a range of behaviours, because their calls will have evolved from the repertoire of a shared ancestor, and these parallels are called homologies. Certain sounds may have evolved little from ancestral calls, while other sounds differ strongly between closely related species.

An extensive account of parallel repertoires and how bird sounds have evolved within a family is to be found in *Bird sounds and their meaning* by Rosemary Jellis (1977), one of the best introductions to the evolution of sounds. Jellis summarised and developed the work of many researchers who were "cracking the code of bird sound communication". The book draws most of its examples from the tits Paridae and describes the sounds common to the whole family. It then shows how each tit species has evolved some of these common sounds into its own calls and song patterns, using subtle modifications.

It has always annoyed me that Great Tit *Parus major* seems to be the only bird most birders credit with an extensive repertoire. Maybe it's because Great Tit can make sounds that are mistaken for Common Chaffinch or other tits, and many birders have experienced the embarrassment of misidentifying these common species.

It's interesting to explore how tits vary their scolding *chick-a-dee* sounds to create different calls. These are very useful sounds and slight variations are thought to tell one flock from another (Mammen & Nowicki 1981) and where the bird is in relation to others in the flock (Hailman & Ficken 1996). In North America the tits are called 'chickadees' and in a study it was found that when Black-capped Chickadees used calls of this type to mob predators, the length and number of *dee* notes (there is seldom just one) vary according to how dangerous the predator is (Templeton et al 2005). Willow Tit *P montana* used to be considered part of the same superspecies, and its *chick-a-dee* calls vary the number and length of the *dee* notes along similar lines. The *chick-a-dee* sounds are also used as simple songs, or in more varied singing bouts. Listen to the recordings of this type of calls from four different species. In the sonagrams, the *chick-a* notes look like extreme variations of a similarly shaped sound. The *dee-dee-dee*s are all broadband sounds, but with different lengths and delivered at different speeds. These recordings show how the tits have each evolved their own versions of these sounds.

In Dorset, birders have started to worry about the breeding population of Willow Tit. At the same time there is a greater understanding of the identification criteria for both Willow and Marsh Tits *P palustris*; features like wing panels, shape of bib, and overall size no longer stand (Scott 1999). So now it is not certain whether there has been a severe reduction in the breeding population of Willow Tit or there has been a change in the way people separate them. In other words, whether many sightings in the past concerned misidentified Marsh Tits. Fortunately, the differences in the *chick-a-dee* sounds are diagnostic.

Willow Tit's *chick-a-dee*s are the most noticeable calls in its repertoire, and tend to be just a robust, consistently slow, series of long *dee*s. Unlike Marsh Tit they don't always start with their high-pitched, short *chick-a* (**CD1-67**). The equivalent calls of Marsh Tit do start with a sharper, whiplash *chick-a*, and the repeated *dee* notes are much shorter. They are also delivered more rapidly and while this varies with the degree of the bird's excitement, the speed is typically twice that of Willow. Compare the *dee* notes in the sonagrams; those of Willow are like solid tower blocks with regular gaps in between. The weaker 'Eiffel' towers of Marsh show that its *dee* notes are less harsh, and the higher pitch of the fundamental makes the timbre sound less aggressive. This combined with the rapid delivery gives the impression of Marsh being a more excitable bird, although the sound is less distinctive (**CD1-68**).

CD1-67   **Willow Tit** *Poecile montana* Huizen, Noord-Holland, Netherlands, 14:56, 13 February 2003. *Chick-a-dee* type calls recorded in a larch plantation. 03.001.AB.10713.02

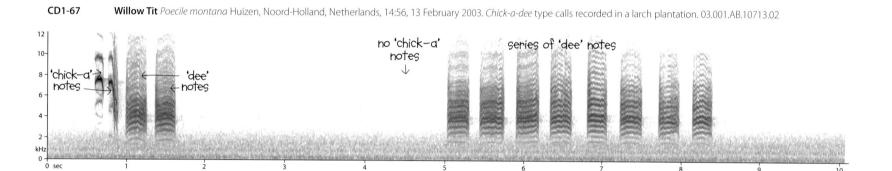

CD1-68   **Marsh Tit** *Poecile palustris* Leuvenumse Bos, Gelderland, Netherlands, 08:10, 8 April 2000. *Chick-a-dee* type calls uttered from high oak canopy. Background: Great Spotted Woodpecker *Dendrocopos major*, Song Thrush *Turdus philomelos* and Winter Wren *Troglodytes troglodytes*. 00.001.AB.05428.01

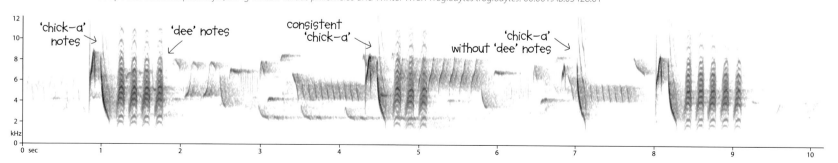

Arnoud recorded the alarmed Great Tit in the next recording while waiting for a Eurasian Pygmy Owl *Glaucidium passerinum* to call in southern Germany (**CD1-69**). At 7 kHz, the *chick-a* is very high pitched and will be missed by some of us, while the *dee* notes have a low-pitched fundamental and a rapid delivery. The European Blue Tit *Cyanistes caeruleus* in **CD1-70** has a much faster variant of the same sound, in this case being used to scold the Eurasian Jay *Garrulus glandarius* in the background. Its *chick-a* sounds can be varied in all regards. Sometimes they are repeated several times or dropped for several phrases, and while high pitched, they are easy to hear. In the sonagrams, the *dee-dee-dee*s vary in thickness (length) and subtly rise in pitch, dropping from the high pitched *chick-a* and rising at the end. This seems very different from the simple *dee-dee-dee*s of Great, Willow and Marsh Tit. Now as you cast your eye over all the sonagrams, you should be able to see the relationships and the variations quite clearly.

CD1-69 **Great Tit** *Parus major* Grainau, Eibsee, Bayern, Germany, 07:51, 4 April 2003. *Chick-a-dee* type calls in response to a Eurasian Pygmy Owl, a very dangerous predator for a Great Tit. 03.005.AB.12059.11

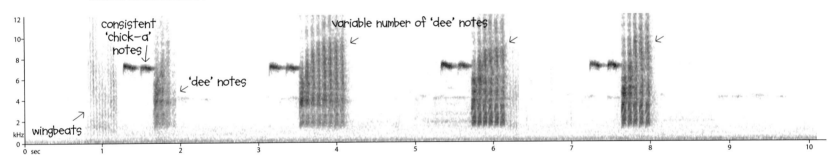

CD1-70 **European Blue Tit** *Cyanistes caeruleus*, Posterholt, Limburg, Netherlands, 08:31, 2 May 2000. *Chick-a-dee* type calls, probably in response to a Eurasian Jay *Garrulus glandarius*. 00.004.AB.13959.31

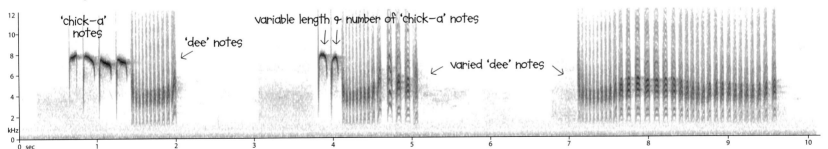

Parallel lines

Closely related pairs of birds have parallel repertoires, a series of equivalent sounds that can be used in similar circumstances. Working through these enables you to decide which comparisons are the easiest for identification and where a sound is diagnostic. To illustrate this, we chose to take a close look at the sounds of adult Arctic Tern *S paradisaea* and Common Tern *S hirundo*. Getting the recordings needed for this section involved a lot of travelling. While I have hundreds of Common Terns breeding nearby on Brownsea Island, Dorset, I don't have Arctic Terns, and anyway for recording purposes it is very noisy. Near Killian's home in Wexford, there are sites for both species. Magnus and I visited Killian a number of times and we should have been able to make all the recordings for this comparison. Unfortunately, when you visit a mixed tern colony, the sounds seem to be an impenetrable chaos of endless variations and, in the best month of August, Killian lures you away to look for vagrants at Tacumshin. Then when you get home you realise that you're still missing some recordings. So far, The Sound Approach has visited 42 countries and this eight track section involved no less than five of them. We used two recordings from Wexford, while the others are from Kazachstan, Norway (the northern reaches of Finnmark), Spain, and finally birds recorded in Orkney and Shetland, Scotland. The five of us have travelled almost as far as an old Arctic Tern.

Only when I take the time to listen carefully at home to these recordings do the sounds become a reliable means of separating these very similar-looking species. The three most useful vocalisations for separating adult Arctic and Common Terns are long calls, advertising calls and *kip* calls. We've also shown scolding *gyarrrr* calls to illustrate a similar shared sound.

Common Tern *Sterna hirundo*, adult summer, Our Lady's Island Lake, Wexford, Ireland, 16 July 2001 *(Killian Mullarney)*

The simplest way to tell the two species apart vocally is the striking difference between the long calls. The long call of Common Tern **(CD1-71)** was recorded over Our Lady's Island Lake in Wexford. It's a rapid series of *kearrip* notes that speed up towards the end. Imagine skimming a stone across the lake and as the skips become closer and closer and lower and lower that's how the sound speeds up with each note getting a little lower. The Arctic Tern's long call **(CD1-72)** always consists of a repeating pattern containing a couple of staccato notes followed by a longer one: *da-da-daaa*, like a morse code SOS being tapped out with increasing urgency by a Norwegian resistance worker in a second world war movie.

CD1-71 **Common Tern** *Sterna hirundo* Our Lady's Island Lake, Wexford, Ireland, 20:40, 14 July 2003. Long calls as two birds meet in the air. Background: distant Roseate Tern *S dougallii* and Arctic *Tern S paradisaea.* 03.012.KM.03730.01

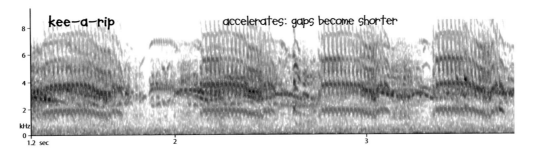

CD1-72 **Arctic Tern** *Sterna paradisaea* Faerøy, Røstlandet, Lofoten, Norway, 08:25, 12 July 2001. A fairly slow long call by an individual standing near its nest along the seashore on a misty morning. Background: Common Eider *Somateria mollissima*, Eurasian Oystercatcher *Haematopus ostralegus*, Ruddy Turnstone *Arenaria interpres*, Common Gull *Larus canus* and Herring Gull *Larus argentatus.* 01.012.AB.10227.02

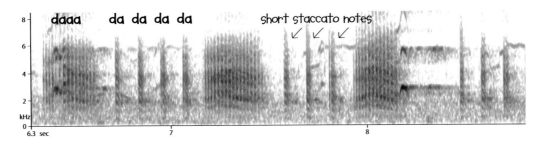

A relaxed and confident Arctic or Common Tern, flying from A to B, or just fishing, will often give calls that BWP have named *advertising calls* at fairly regular intervals, typically at a rate of about two every three seconds. Research has shown that these calls identify the individual, enabling a fledgling tern to recognise its own parent bringing fish. For us, these calls are not quite so easy to separate (**CD1-73 and 74**). The key differences between these two species' sounds are pitch, speed of delivery, and length of note. Taking the geographical mnemonic to its furthest point: our Spanish Common Tern takes it a little slower, lower and longer, more mellow comparatively, *keearr..*, while the Norwegian Arctic Tern is sharper at first but then harsher, shorter and more hurried *irrr*.

CD1-73   **Common Tern** *Sterna hirundo* Ebro delta, Catalunya, Spain, 19:19, 6 June 2002. Adult flying overhead, passing a sand bar on vast Mediterranean beach. Background: begging calls. 02.014.AB.12210.01

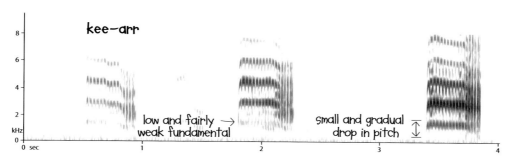

CD1 74   **Arctic Tern** *Sterna paradisaea* Between Vardø and Vadsø, Finnmark, Norway, 5 June 2002. Single adult crossing the tundra. Background: Common Eider *Somateria mollissima*, Red-necked Phalarope *Phalaropus lobatus* and Black-legged Kittiwake Rissa *tridactyla*. 02.013.MC.13100.01

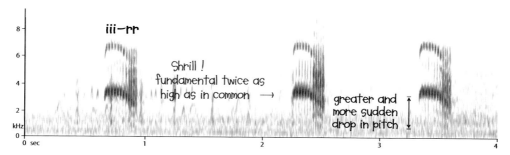

When terns fly up and around you, scolding but not actually attacking, fewer advertising calls will be heard, and a more deliberate and harsher *gyarrrrr*, similar in both species, will become the dominant sound. This call is a variation on the advertising call and so again is slightly lower pitched in Common Tern (**CD1-75**) than in Arctic Tern (**CD1-76**), but this is only really noticeable in the fundamental frequency of the start of the call. Although not very helpful for species identification, it helps to distinguish this generic call from the more helpful advertising calls.

CD1-75   **Common Tern** *Sterna hirundo* Steppes near Korgalzhyn, Aqmola Oblast, Kazakhstan, 07:34, 24 May 2003. Passing adult pauses to scold the recordist from a perch on a telegraph wire. Background: European Bee-eater *Merops apiaster*, Eurasian Skylark *Alauda arvensis*, Sand Martin *Riparia riparia*, Sykes's Blue-headed Wagtail *Motacilla flava beema*, Bluethroat *Luscinia svecica* and Common Rosefinch *Carpodacus erythrinus*. 03.020.MR.01122.00

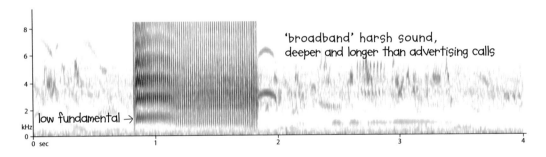

CD1-76   **Arctic Tern** *Sterna paradisaea* South Ronaldsay, Orkney, Scotland, 13 July 2001. Several adults scold the recordist with angry *gyarrrrr* calls. Background: Common Gull *Larus canus*. 01.032.MR.15622.01

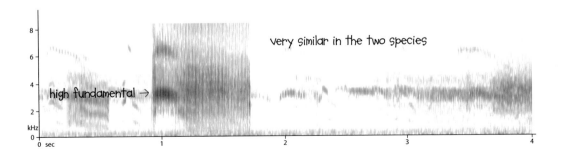

Kip calls (**CD1-77 and 78**) can be heard in a variety of excited situations, typically involving retreat or departure. The pitch is again the key for identification here with the Arctic Tern higher pitched than the Common Tern.

CD1-77   **Common Tern** *Sterna hirundo* Our Lady's Island Lake, Wexford, Ireland, 9 July 2004. *Kip* calls during an aggressive interaction at a colony, heard best at the start. A rattle followed by a growl (heard for example at 0:02, 0:03 and 0:05) is given while actually attacking; *kip* calls are given while backing off. 04.001.KM.12930.10

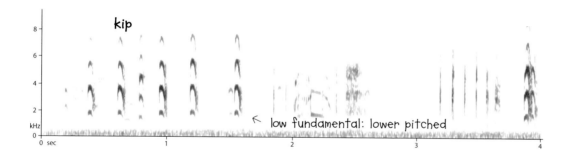

CD1-78   **Arctic Tern** *Sterna paradisaea* Fetlar, Shetland, Scotland, early morning, 10 July 2001. Several adults in flight and resting at small loch in tundra-like moorland. *Kip* calls (best at start and 0:14), *gyarrrrr* calls, advertising calls, long calls etc. Background: Dunlin *Calidris alpina*, Eurasian Skylark *Alauda arvensis* and Meadow Pipit *Anthus pratensis*. 01.032.MR.04044.11

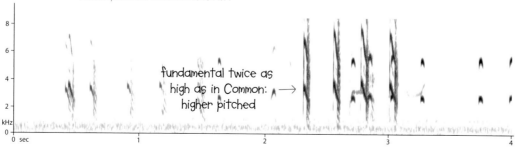

Different species can share very similar sounds

If a particular sound is exactly right for a basic need, several species may use it even if they are not closely related. One of the first examples of this was described by Marler (1959) when he showed that many passerines (eg, Dunnock *Prunella modularis*, Common Blackbird, Common Chaffinch) use a high-pitched *seep* call in the presence of certain predators, especially hawks. He explained that the high frequency and drawn out nature of the call, as well as the soft start and end, give the call ventriloquial qualities. All three features of the sound make it very difficult for a predator to tell the location of the caller. At the same time, all the small birds in the vicinity are warned about the threat, and can take evasive action or just keep perfectly still. Listen to the examples of *seep* calls from unrelated songbirds: a Bohemian Waxwing *Bombycilla garrulus* in Iceland that has seen a Merlin *F columbarius* (**CD1-79a**), and a Ring Ouzel *T torquatus* in Turkey that can see and hear the Long-legged Buzzard *Buteo rufinus* calling very distantly in the background (**CD1-79b**). As an example of *seep* calls from a very common bird, listen to a European Robin *Erithacus rubecula* recorded in northern Scotland (**CD1-79c**). Often a cat, or in this case the recordist, is enough to stimulate calls of this kind.

CD1-79a   **Bohemian Waxwing** *Bombycilla garrulus* Hliðarendi, Ölfus, southern Iceland, 21 October 2004.
0:00 – 0:51   *Seep* calls given in an alert posture while a Merlin was hunting nearby. Background: Common Raven *Corvus corax*. 04.042.MR.12326.20

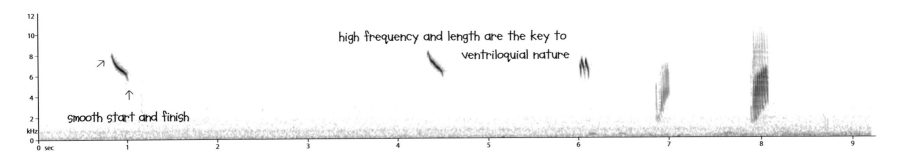

CD1-79b   **Ring Ouzel** *Turdus torquatus* Sivrikaya, Rize, Turkey, 23 May 2002. A male paused briefly during a bout of quiet singing and gave these *seep* calls as a Long-legged Buzzard
0:53 – 1:11   *Buteo rufinus* flew nearby (the latter's calls can be heard very faintly). It started singing its simple paired notes again near the end. Background: Dunnock *Prunella modularis*,
      Bright-green Warbler *Phylloscopus nitidus*, Caucasian Chiffchaff *Phylloscopus lorenzii* and Common Rosefinch *Carpodacus erythrinus*. 02.026.MR.00732.01

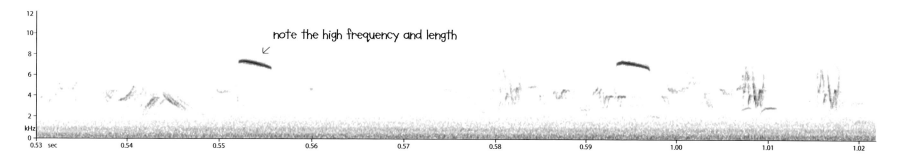

note the high frequency and length

CD1-79c   **European Robin** *Erithacus rubecula* Abernethy Forest, Highland, Scotland, 17 July 2001. Very high-pitched *seep* calls probably in reaction to the recordist. Background: wind
1:13 – 1:33   in pine trees. 01.033.MR.15007.01

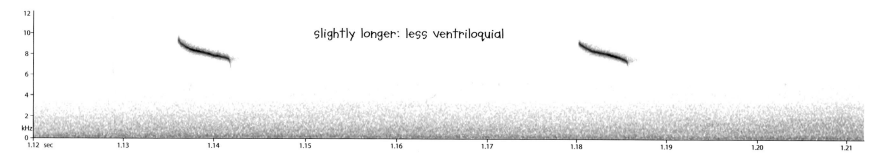

slightly longer: less ventriloquial

One time while I was sitting in Białowieza forest in Poland listening for woodpeckers, I became aware of Common Chaffinches scolding. When I looked, I found a pair attacking a Great Spotted Woodpecker, which can be a predator of eggs and nestlings (**CD1-80a**). Calls used aggressively as threats can be very similar between unrelated species, and nearly always are used at close range, loud and harsh-sounding in most birds. To an opponent, the sound is literally 'in your face'; by using as many frequencies as possible a bird makes itself seem more powerful, more present, like a cat making its fur stand on end to look bigger. One aspect of making recordings is that you can make comments on the tape as a note for later. The disadvantage to this is all your mistakes are there for posterity. When I recorded the Corn Buntings *Emberiza calandra* on Mallorca in **CD1-80b**, I can hear myself saying; "male came to chat with another male that had been singing". On reflection, male birds during the breeding season don't usually chat: they

Common Chaffinch *Fringilla coelebs* Białowieza forest, Podłaskie, Poland, 09:41, 4 May 2005. Pair threatening a Great Spotted Woodpecker *Dendrocopos major* with harsh threat calls and *pink* calls. The woodpecker can be heard giving a few *pic* calls. Background: Three-toed Woodpecker *Picoides tridactylus* distant drumming, Common Blackbird *Turdus merula*, Blackcap *Sylvia atricapilla*, Wood Warbler *Phylloscopus sibilatrix* and Common Chiffchaff *P collybita*. (See sonagram below that of CD2-54a.) 05.008.MC.03230.01

CD1-80a
0:00 – 0:41

argue, and sure enough the harsh calls from four seconds into the recording sound almost identical to the calls we heard in the chaffinch recording. Listen to another example, recorded while hoping for a Pine Grosbeak *Pinicola enucleator* at a bird feeder outside a hotel in Lapland. In this case, European Goldfinches are threatening each other, as they squabble over food (**CD1-80c**). The goldfinches deliver the calls with the same noisy use of a broad range of frequencies, but with a different more rattling rhythm.

CD1-80b
0:43 – 0:57

Corn Bunting *Emberiza calandra* Can Sureda, Mallorca, Spain, 16 April 2000. An interaction between two males. Background: Zitting Cisticola *Cisticola juncidis* and European Greenfinch *Chloris chloris*. 00.004.MC.02325.01

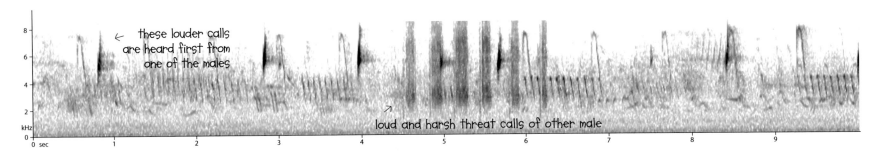

Calls of this type are not limited to songbirds, and the *gyarrrrr* scolding calls of Arctic and Common Terns fit this category (**CD1-75 and 76**). You can even hear something similar in some wildfowl. I particularly enjoyed making the next recording in Norwegian Lapland, sitting sheltered from the wind by a large rock facing a sunny tundra pool with several broods of Common Eider *Somateria mollissima*, three female Red-necked Phalaropes *Phalaropus lobatus*, some Ruff *Philomachus pugnax* and a pair of copulating Parasitic Jaegers *Stercorarius parasiticus*. Just when the eider were on the point of leaving the water, a Hooded Crow *C cornix* showed up, possibly interested in their young. The females barked at it angrily and all the eider, young and old, got back in the water (**CD1-81**). As a sonagram shows, the calls the eider used to threaten the crow are like a much deeper version of the other threat calls you already heard; and the noisy structure, maximising the range of frequencies used, is very similar.

Common Eider *Somateria mollissima* Between Vardø and Vadsø, Finnmark, Norway, 5 June 2002. Several females leading their broods call harshly to repel a Hooded Crow. The young are responsible for the continuous peeping sounds. Background: Eurasian Oystercatcher *Haematopus ostralegus* and heavy breathing of the recordist. 02.013.MC.12501.31   CD1-81

CD1-80c
0:59 – 1:09

European Goldfinch *Carduelis carduelis* Poole, Dorset, England, 07:30, 15 January 2004. One bird threatens another at feeder. 04.001.MC.11615.02

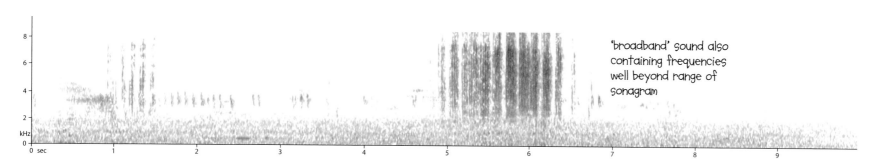

'broadband' sound also containing frequencies well beyond range of sonagram

When a predator passes through a flock of birds, those in the path of the predator are silent, and those it has flown past call more as it passes and less as the danger recedes. Thus an individual in the flock can work out where the danger is and in which direction it is moving (Dabelsteen & McGregor 1996). Listen to an example of this 'call contagion' as a Eurasian Sparrowhawk *Accipiter nisus* passes through a large flock of Long-tailed Tits *Aegithalos caudatus* and 'common crossbills' *Loxia curvirostra* (**CD1-82**). You can't actually hear the sparrowhawk itself, but you can hear successively closer Long-tailed Tits beginning to call, until at a certain point the crossbills explode in all directions from the pine top they had been feeding in. The penetrating sound of all the Long-tailed Tits calling at the same time works as an anti-predator strategy like

seep alarm calls. Very high-pitched, and coming from many directions at once, the sound makes it difficult for the sparrowhawk to single out a victim (Thielcke 1976).

This type of *strategic* use of sound has been taken a step further by Les Beletsky who wrote an excellent book on his studies of Red-winged Blackbirds (Beletsky 1996). As he watched and listened to these birds calling constantly while moving about in the colony he noticed that as danger appeared on the outskirts, the first bird to discover the threat would change whatever call it had been using to another in its repertoire. Each bird would then change to the same call, in a wave radiating through the colony from the direction of the perceived danger. If a threat then appeared from another direction they would change call again.

CD1-82   **Long-tailed Tit** *Aegithalos caudatus* and **'common crossbills'** *Loxia curvirostra* Bakkum, Noord-Holland, Netherlands, 14:00, 18 November 2005. A flock of Parakeet Crossbills *L c* type X and a few Glip Crossbills *L c* type C are cracking cones in the top of a pine tree. As a Eurasian Sparrowhawk zeroes in for an attack, a wave of high-pitched rippling call contagion passes through the spread-out flock of Long-tailed Tits in the surroundings, tracing the sparrowhawk's trajectory, until the crossbills erupt from the pine in all directions, dropping their pine cones to the ground. Background: Common Blackbird *Turdus merula* also startled by the attack. 05.031.MR.20150.20

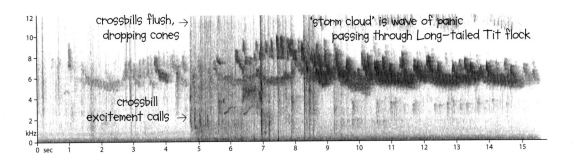

He thought that there was no particular pattern to the choice of call as long as it was different from the dominant call being given by the colony before the danger arrived. As Les writes, "The lesson that redwing alert calls brings to these analyses is that, **although one species may have a large number of signals, they do not necessarily have different meanings or functions**".

Rails have an even greater need for this kind of strategy; foraging in channels deep in the marsh they can't see danger easily as it flies above them. Water Rails *Rallus aquaticus* squeal readily whenever a loud noise occurs. Try clapping your hands anywhere near them to test this. In this recording that I made in the Albuferita marsh on Mallorca you can hear Water Rails in alarm as five Eleonora's Falcons *F eleonorae* fly overhead (**CD1-83**).

Lost for words?

For birders, one of the biggest challenges in bird sounds is to be able to communicate specific and accurate descriptions of songs and calls. A good description can contain a lot of information. Try this one by Mike Rogers (1978), the secretary of the British rarities committee (both then and now), where he describes the difference between Goldcrest and Firecrest *R ignicapilla* contact calls: "I have always found that the normal contact or feeding call of the Goldcrest is indeed the familiar 'zeec' or 'zee' sound, but careful listening reveals that the full call consists of five such notes delivered at regular intervals and all at the same pitch. On the other hand, the equivalent 'zit' calls of the Firecrest are not only generally fuller and coarser in tone, but are also linked quite differently than Goldcrest. Again there are five notes, but there is

CD1-83   **Water Rail** *Rallus aquaticus* Albuferita, Mallorca, Spain, 26 May 2003. Call contagion: several rails call as an Fleonora's Falcon flies over their part of the marsh. Background: Common Moorhen *Gallinula chloropus*, Eurasian Coot *Fulica atra*, Cetti's Warbler *Cettia cetti* and Zitting *Cisticola Cisticola juncidis*. 03.017.MC.14500.12

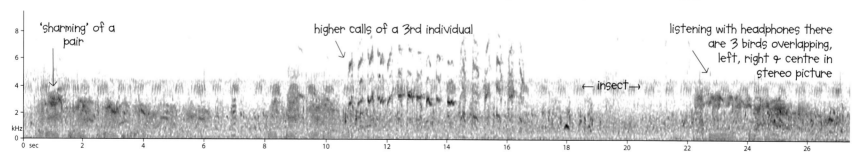

a strong stress on the first and it is noticeably longer in duration than any of the subsequent four, which are of equal length and interval to those of Goldcrest. These four notes, however, are in fact on a slightly rising scale, which is perfectly easy to discern. …".

These kind of careful descriptions enable others to enter the discussion. Listen to the examples of both 'crests' calling during autumn migration **(CD1-84 and 85)**. All we can add in the light of modern understanding is to question whether these sounds are a series of calls or might actually constitute a very simple kind of song.

Consider your use of the word song or call carefully, and describe what the bird in question was doing when you heard it. Try to avoid assuming any particular sound is always used in the same way. Opt for 'call heard when it took off' rather than 'the flight call'. Or 'call used while mobbing a kestrel' rather than 'the mobbing call'. Describing the context in which a sound was heard is essential in any attempt to talk about bird vocalisations. Be aware of how your distance from the bird and the prevalent acoustics may have degraded the sound before it reached your ears. Was it a powerful sound or a weak one? When using commercial recordings as a reference, remember that the bird

CD1-84   **Goldcrest** *Regulus regulus* IJmuiden, Noord-Holland, Netherlands, 17 November 2001. Calls of an autumn migrant. Background: Lesser Black-backed Gull *Larus fuscus*, European Robin *Erithacus rubecula*, Fieldfare *Turdus pilaris* and Eurasian Magpie *Pica pica*. 01.043.MR.01819.01

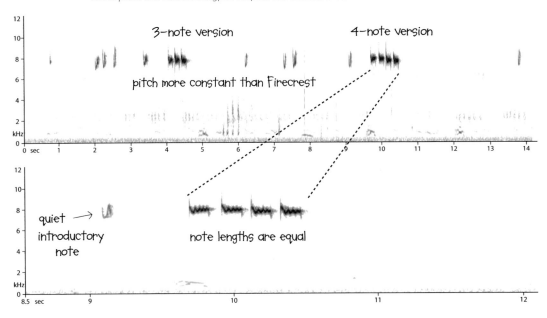

may sound quite different under field conditions, and probably not as loud. If you are unable to make your own recording of a sound, take notes on the pitch and rhythm as accurately as you can, also noting the length of gaps between the sounds. Compare other bird sounds you know better. Try developing your own freehand sonagram style. It doesn't matter if your 'sonagram' is a far cry from the one your computer comes up with.

Firecrest *Regulus ignicapilla*, Hook Head, Wexford, Ireland, 5 November 1987 *(Killian Mullarney)*

CD1-85   **Firecrest** *Regulus ignicapilla* IJmuiden, Noord-Holland, Netherlands, 29 September 2002. Two autumn migrants, one near and one far, calling to each other from a distance. Background: Common Chiffchaff *Phylloscopus collybita*, European Blue Tit *Cyanistes caeruleus* and Eurasian Magpie *Pica pica*. 02.042.MR.12628.02

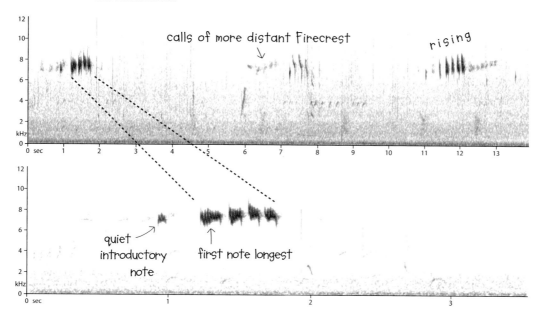

Part 5: Hamish taught me all he knows about bird sounds

Ageing bird sounds

Hamish Murray and I first met in March 1980 shortly after he had seen a Black-browed Albatross *Thalassarche melanophris* passing Durlston Country Park, Dorset, where he was the warden. We've been good friends since. At the time I wanted to learn bird sounds and cycled the 15 miles in the dark to be there at dawn in order to be able to walk round with him as he surveyed the singing birds. This then started my obsessive love affair with Durlston that lasted more than a decade. I learnt a lot of things, and saw a lot of birds for the first time.

Hamish's grasp of bird sounds is very good; his talents as an artist and musician give him an enviable breadth of observational skills. Despite playing guitar in a local rock band he still has good high frequency hearing. Oddly, he never got on well with bird tapes and it constantly intrigued me that he could never recognise bird sounds I played from tapes. As he had no problem recognising the real sounds in the field, I started to realise that recorded bird sounds seldom sounded like the real thing. Hamish is a passionate patch watcher with an intense interest in visible migration, which I share. It was while watching large flocks of passing finches together one autumn that he pointed out a call as a juvenile Common Linnet. Ageing bird calls was not something that I had given much thought to. I started to read up on the subject and soon learnt that most sounds develop over a bird's life starting, amazingly, in the egg. Birds attempt to sing when a few weeks old, and calls develop through a series of juvenile sounds into the full adult repertoire.

That birds' sounds vary dependent on their age and sex is the basis on which The Sound Approach is built. Reading bird guides and identification papers where this is ignored is like identifying birds today with S Vere Benson's *Observer's book of birds* (1952), which shows Green *T ochropus* and Wood Sandpiper *T glareola* with just one black-and-white illustration for both and a mention in the text that the Wood Sandpiper's legs are lighter.

To take these thoughts a little further, I first need to explain a couple of terms: *oscines* and *non-oscines*. Oscine, based on Latin *oscen*, means singing bird. In an Old World context, oscines are simply passerines so non-oscines are everything before larks in the *Collins bird guide*. But in a global context, oscine and passerine are not synonymous. In the New World some passerine families (including the tyrant flycatchers Tyrannidae some of which occur as vagrants in the Western Palearctic) are classed as *suboscines*. It has long been thought that oscines learn their songs and some calls, while in suboscines and non-oscines the sounds are innate. This is important to us, because if the sounds that we use to identify birds were all genetically pre-programmed, like plumages and skeletal structure, then sound identification would be much more straightforward. Keeping parrots in captivity led to the early realisation that these non-oscines could learn sounds too, and later hummingbirds and the suboscine bellbirds (eg, Kroodsma 2005) had to be added to the exceptions. I believe that as researchers keep investigating these non-learners they will find more and more exceptions. Two researchers, Meredith West and Andrew King (West & King 1996), have now suggested that suboscines such as the New World flycatchers may learn their much simpler sounds very quickly, and perhaps we will find out that this applies to some of the non-oscines as well. As a general rule, however, oscines have the most complex and varied repertoires, and it is with this group that we need to be most alert to age-related variation.

As we will see, an awareness of how bird sounds mature can be an important aid in bird identification. The development of all vocalisations follows a predictable path. Calls within the egg change into calls used to beg for food and other basic necessities, and then they diversify, and change into adult calls and songs. This was first described by Nicholson (Nicholson & Koch 1936), and first explored in real detail by Thorpe (1961).

The egg

I am still amazed that ducklings in the egg have been shown to be able to hear their mother for a week before they hatch. Once the eggs are pipped and air can get in, Goethe (1937, 1955) discovered that Herring Gulls will call from the egg when the colony is disturbed or when the egg is shaken. From studies of Mallards *Anas platyrhynchos*, Eurasian Skylarks and other species, it has been shown that many young birds call to each other in the egg and, where it is to their advantage, birds even synchronise hatching by calling to each other (Vince 1969).

Call development

Chicks stimulate their parents to feed them with calls, and in many species young can distinguish their parents' sounds from those of other adults. Sandwich Tern chicks for example start calling when they hear their parents calling above the colony. Rosemary Jellis described work by Tschanz (1968) who showed that young Common Murre *Uria aalge* recognise their parents individually by call. If their own parent doesn't return from the sea after a day or two they seek warmth and food from another adult, stimulating adoption by learning and responding to the new adult's calls.

Using sonagrams, Thielcke (1976) illustrated beautifully the way that begging calls of young Short-toed Treecreeper *Certhia brachydactyla* slowly change in structure over the course of 25 days, until they become adult social calls. He also showed how the adult song consisted of calls arranged in a learnt set sequence and that each sequence was characteristic of a Short-toed population.

In the late eighties I started to concentrate my birding on Poole Harbour, an area of nearly 100 square miles of beautiful scenery and great birds. Around the same time, researcher Robin Ward found a Wilson's Phalarope *P tricolor* in Holes Bay, just outside where I was working. Robin had come from Wales and was surveying for an environmental impact study. He suggested that we started a bird pub to encourage Poole birders to come together, discuss what they had seen and learn more about birds. Over the next 15 years the Poole pub idea flourished and I made some great friends there. In the nineties one of the various puzzles we all discussed was that of autumn Common Chiffchaff call development. Around this time we were all getting very interested in the idea that the chiffchaff could be split into several species, and were listening more carefully than we had before. For two or three autumns, many of us noticed that instead of the normal *huit* we were hearing *wheeoo* calls (**CD1-86**). The suggestion was that chiffchaffs had changed their common call. Was it a different population that was now passing through, and might they even represent a different taxon that had previously been overlooked?

I had read in BWP that young Common Chiffchaffs (of the nominate subspecies *P c collybita*) had different calls. Then one autumn day, while birding with Paul Holt on Ballard Down overlooking Poole Harbour, the conversation turned to juvenile calls. We heard a chiffchaff giving the anomalous *wheeoo* call and Paul commented that he also thought that this was the characteristic call of a young bird. After this autumn, however, birds calling this way seemed to stop showing up: there were very few for several years. What had happened? Surely, if they were first-year birds we would hear lots of them every autumn?

Common Chiffchaff *Phylloscopus collybita*, juvenile, Murrintown, Wexford, Ireland, 11 August 1989 *(Killian Mullarney)*

By this time the subject had started to intrigue quite a few birders, and Bill Oddie (1997) even suggested in his 'Gripping yarns' column in Birdwatch, that we might be witnessing the birth of a new species. I discussed the likelihood of them being something exotic with Martin Cade, the warden of Portland bird observatory, Dorset, who was catching 100s of chiffchaffs. He

CD1-86 **Common Chiffchaff** *Phylloscopus collybita collybita* IJmuiden, Noord-Holland, Netherlands, 9 September 2004. *Wheeoo* calls of a presumed first-year bird These calls are typical of many young Common Chiffchaffs from about late August until late autumn, and occasionally into the next spring. Background: Winter Wren *Troglodytes troglodytes* and Dunnock *Prunella modularis*. 04.042.MR.04023.01

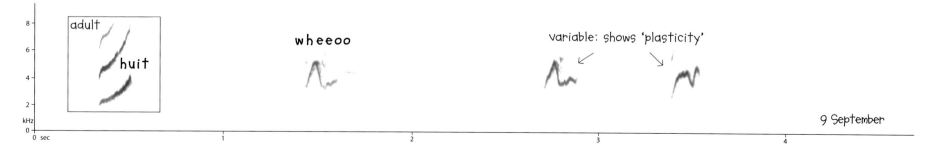

told me that several of the birds which had called *wheeoo* upon release had shown all the in-hand characters of the nominate. Killian then clinched it for me when he took a dictaphone into his garden in Wexford, and recorded an adult feeding young giving *wheeoo* calls.

The debate was still not over, however, and whenever I tried to argue the case for the sound being that of a young bird I could never explain why the calls were now heard far less commonly than in some previous autumns. Then it occurred to me that perhaps the wave of chiffchaffs we encounter at coastal migration hotspots in Britain might differ in their stage of vocal development from year to year. The autumns when we are flooded with chiffchaffs using *wheeoo* calls could be those where there are large numbers of late broods, either caused by poor springs on the breeding grounds or, alternatively, by a favourable breeding season resulting in large numbers of second broods. Other years, chiffchaffs might be a little older by the time they pass through, with most of them already giving adult-like *hueet* calls. When we age birds we do so mainly by plumage. Usually, this relies on a very straightforward set of criteria, and when a songbird is moulting it typically does so either before migrating or afterwards, when it has arrived at its wintering grounds. Unlike moult, call development has no bearing on the ability of a bird to migrate. Until this point I had failed to realise the obvious, that these two kinds of development could proceed independently, each at their own pace.

Listen to a recording of a Common Chiffchaff at a very early stage of development **(CD1-87)**, a juvenile on the 3rd of August. At this stage, calls of the nominate can sound remarkably similar to those of adult Siberian Chiffchaff (*tristis*), as you can see in the sonagram (compare with the Siberian Chiffchaff of CD1-15). These calls are typical of the first couple of weeks after fledging, so they shouldn't be a problem in places where *tristis* turns up in October. Returning to CD1-86, which was recorded during autumn migration on the 9th of September, most of the calls in

CD1-87   **Common Chiffchaff** *Phylloscopus collybita collybita* IJmuiden, Noord-Holland, Netherlands, 3 August 2004. *Whee* calls of a Common Chiffchaff only a few weeks old. From time to time the calls are more inflected, and you can hear hints of adult calls at times (0:27-0:35). It is normal for calls of such a young songbird to be rather 'wobbly', and this is even more apparent when the bird makes some of its first attempts to sing (0:24-0:26 and 0:52-0:55). Background: Herring Gull *Larus argentatus*, Lesser Black-backed Gull *L fuscus*, Winter Wren *Troglodytes troglodytes*, Common Nightingale *Luscinia megarhynchos*, Willow Warbler *Phylloscopus trochilus*, Eurasian Magpie *Pica pica* and Common Linnet *Carduelis cannabina*. 04.038.MR.15247.01

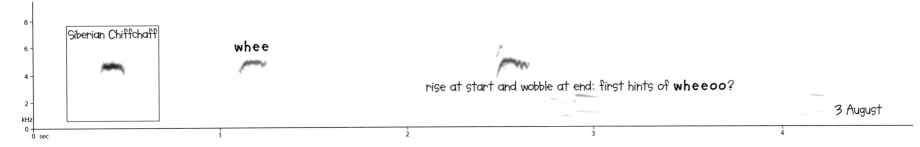

it could be described as *wheeoo*, but a few are less inflected (eg, 0:16-0:18), and reminiscent of the early stage you can hear in CD1-87. A call of an adult Common Chiffchaff from CD1-13 is shown for comparison.

As you now hear, sound development is not straightforward, and can appear to move forward and back. A practical aspect to this is that in spring, both adult males and females will sometimes use immature calls. In chiffchaffs, for example, immature *wheeoo*

calls can sometimes be heard in the spring, quite often interspersed with normal *huit* calls. Adults use immature calls in courtship in the same way we may use baby talk when trying to be endearing. We don't have examples of Common Chiffchaff doing this but we do have these calls given by an adult female Mealy Redpoll *C flammea* in north-eastern Siberia begging for food in the company of two adult males (**CD1-88a**). You can compare them with calls of a begging juvenile in Finnish Lapland (**CD1-88b**).

CD1-88a   **Mealy Redpoll** *Carduelis flammea* Tiksi, Yakutia, Russia, 2 July 2004. An adult female begging in the
0:00 – 0:18   company of two males as a part of a courtship display. Background: Long-tailed Duck *Clangula hyemalis*,
Common Snipe *Gallinago gallinago* and Snow Bunting *Plectrophenax nivalis*. 04.036.MR.10936.12

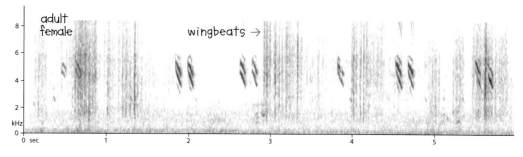

CD1-88b   **Mealy Redpoll** *Carduelis flammea* Utsjoki, Lapland, Finland, 7 June 2003. A juvenile begging for food at
0:20 – 0:53   a feeder in a hotel garden. Background: Willow Warbler *Phylloscopus trochilus*, Pied Flycatcher *Ficedula
hypoleuca* and other redpolls *Carduelis*. 03.022.MC.00300.01

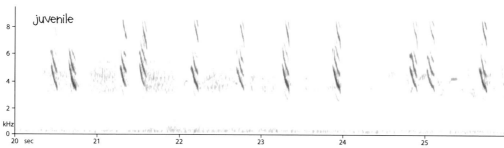

Learning to sing

During another Poole bird pub session in August 1995, I was asked by ringer Dave Dicker why, that day when he had ringed a Cetti's Warbler he knew to be a fresh juvenile, it had flown to a song post and sung. I didn't know the answer, but I looked it up in BWP when I got home and was shocked to read of an endless array of passerines that were known to sing at as little as six weeks old (Goldcrest and Firecrest even start at four weeks). Here is the song of a young Cetti's **(CD1-89)**, and an adult to compare it with **(CD1-90)**.

CD1-89 **Cetti's Warbler** *Cettia cetti* Lake Mikri Prespa, West Macedonia, Greece, 15 July 1999. Subsong of a juvenile. Background: Common Blackbird *Turdus merula* and Cirl Bunting *Emberiza cirlus*. 99.021.MR.11508.12

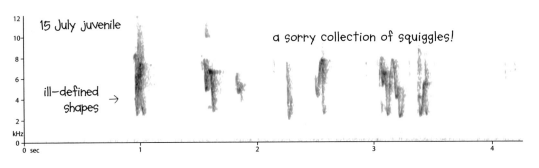

CD1-90 **Cetti's Warbler** *Cettia cetti* Parc Natural S'Albufera, Mallorca, Spain, 1 April 2003. A single very loud territorial song at dusk. Perhaps because of the effort required to sing so loud, adult Cetti's usually only sing once every couple of minutes or so. Background: Western Swamp-hen *Porphyrio porphyrio*, Great Reed Warbler *Acrocephalus arundinaceus* and Great Tit *Parus major*. 03.008.MR.03355.00

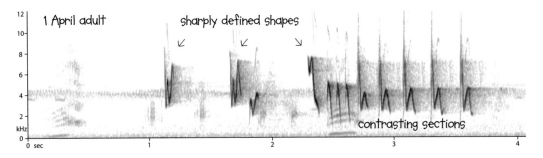

That winter, while listening to *Songs of the warblers* (Borror & Gunn 1985) as I attempted to learn American warbler songs for the *World Series of Birding* race in New Jersey in May, I read what has to be the most comprehensive set of sleeve notes ever. In a few paragraphs it was explained why the sounds I could hear in New Jersey's Cape May woods were not always those on the tapes. "By the time they reach Canada's southern boundaries in spring, most warblers that nest in the north are singing their primary songs. This is not the case, however, in much of the United States, where many warbler species are seen only on migration, and may not have perfected their primary songs."

These things had always interested me, and over the subsequent years I learnt that the stages of song development I had read about in 'American warblers' also apply for many European bird families. I also discovered that in the earlier stages, songs could be produced by both sexes, although after a few months, at least in many species, the females stop singing.

I suspect that there is a great deal more for scientists to learn about the strategies behind song development. The learning process leading to adult song is highly flexible, and has several identifiable stages. At present it is thought that the first of these is *subsong*, where there are hardly any recognisable features of adult song. Gradually, rudiments of adult song start to fall into place, but in sequences that are far longer and more rambling than in adults. At length, often as late as early spring, a songbird progresses to a stage called *plastic song*, in which songs gradually shorten and phrases begin to become more stereotyped. Songs finally *crystallise* when the breeding season gets going. But even after this, some species continue to learn, in some cases adding new material to their songs for many years.

Subsong

Nicholson (Nicholson & Koch 1936) was the first to use the term *subsong* to describe song of low volume that doesn't seem to have any relevance in territorial arguments, or invoke any hostility in other males. Subsong has great potential to confuse the birder, because it is usually given from dense cover, is often full of mimicry, and may bear little resemblance to familiar adult songs we usually rely on in species identification. It is most common in first-year birds. Listen for a continuous stream of twittering, stammering and babbling, littered with call notes, typically on August and September mornings.

Nice (1943) studied Song Sparrows *Melospiza melodia* as they progressed through various stages of vocalisations. Her descriptions were then defined by Thorpe (1961). The details vary between species but on the whole his description has not needed much improvement since then. Thorpe pointed out that **subsong is quieter, with an entirely different pattern of notes and it includes more call notes and mimicry than 'normal' song does. Song bursts tend to be longer, and the frequency range varies more than in the full song.** Subsongs are typical of birds with a low sexual motivation, for example adults and first-year birds before the breeding season really gets started, or juveniles after it has finished. Listen to autumn subsong of a Common Blackbird hidden deep in a berry-laden Elder bush (**CD1-91**).

Common Blackbird *Turdus merula* Texel, Noord-Holland, Netherlands, 09:00, 18 September 2005. Subsong of a first-winter bird. Background: Dunnock *Prunella modularis*, Fieldfare *Turdus pilaris* and Common Chiffchaff *Phylloscopus collybita*. 05.025.MR.13531.01

CD1-91

Most of us do not pay much attention to these songs, not really understanding what they are, and perhaps preferring to ignore them, like ducks in difficult eclipse plumages. Sometimes, however, like when thrushes tune up in this way in early spring, they can create some confusion as these quiet, warbler-like songs from deep inside a bush are mistaken for, eg, Marsh Warblers.

Plastic song

Plastic songs are clearly recognisable and can be identified to species as long as these have identifiable song phrases. However, the timing will often seem wrong and a bird will run phrases together and then sing normally before dropping back into subsong. Plastic song is louder than subsong and the individual phrases are shorter. Fragments of fully formed adult song are typically intermingled with gentle immature babbling. The timing during the bird's calendar, its age, is important and

birds often start to crystallise their songs after a winter break. Then, a young bird may be spending a lot of its time singing. The term plastic song is derived from the pliable or 'plastic' nature of the notes and motifs in it.

Common Chaffinch has been the subject of much of the research on vocal development, including plastic song. This species begins to resolve the finer details and add a terminal flourish to its song around the time it is establishing itself in its own territory. A Common Chaffinch song without a clearly defined terminal flourish will most likely be a first-year bird singing plastic song. The process of crystallisation gradually takes place under the influence of the songs heard from its new neighbours. Listen to the recording illustrating Common Chaffinch plastic song (CD1-92) made by Dick on a sunny day near the migration watchpoint of Hanko. In most of Europe we take Common Chaffinches for granted but in Finland they are spring migrants arriving in places like Hanko in large numbers. Although it was sunny, the temperature was -10ºC.

CD1-92   **Common Chaffinch** *Fringilla coelebs* Täktom, Hanko, Uusimaa, Finland, 11:00, 14 March 2005. Plastic song: either a wintering bird or one of the first new arrivals in spring. Background: European Greenfinch *Chloris chloris* and Yellowhammer *Emberiza citrinella*. 05.001.DF.10130.02

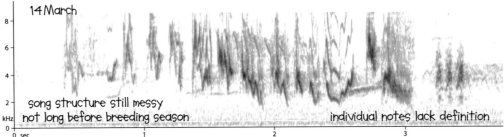

Common Nightingale illustrates the three stages well. Its subsong (CD1-93) is quieter and has an entirely different pattern of notes compared to adult song; it also includes more call notes than a normal song does, including lots of chattering ones, as well as a short whistle near the start, and rattles towards the end. In the case of nightingale, subsong doesn't include more mimicry because adult nightingales already include so much in their songs. Neither are the song bursts longer, but when he described subsong, Thorpe was writing about Common Chaffinch in which the normal song bursts are shorter. The frequency range of the nightingale's subsong is greater than usual in normal song.

Now progress to plastic song (CD1-94) which unlike Common Nightingale's subsong does fit the textbook description. You can hear the song starting to crystallise as it progresses from subsong. The timing isn't right and the phrases run together, then it does sing normally before dropping back into subsong. This plastic song is louder than the earlier example of subsong and the individual phrases have become shorter, and fragments of fully formed adult song are intermingled with gentle immature babbling. This could be mistaken for Thrush Nightingale.

Finally listen to a beautiful, fully crystallised song of Common Nightingale, recorded by Arnoud near his home in the Netherlands. It includes long gaps between phrases, allowing the singer to listen to responses from its neighbours (CD1-95).

Common Nightingale *Luscinia megarhynchos* IJmuiden, Noord-Holland, Netherlands, 4 August 2004. Subsong of a juvenile. Background: Lesser Black-backed Gull *Larus fuscus*, rising whistles of another Common Nightingale, Willow Warbler *Phylloscopus trochilus*, Common Starling *Sturnus vulgaris* and Common Reed Bunting *Emberiza schoeniclus*. 04.038.MR.15901.11   CD1-93

Common Nightingale *Luscinia megarhynchos* Paphos Headland, Paphos, Cyprus, 10 April 2000. Almost continuous plastic song of a spring migrant. Background: juvenile Great Tits *Parus major*. 00.016.MR.02731.01   CD1-94

Common Nightingale *Luscinia megarhynchos* Kennemerduinen, Bloemendaal, Noord-Holland, Netherlands, 03:05, 19 May 2005. Nocturnal song of an adult. Background: other Common Nightingales and Common Grasshopper Warbler *Locustella naevia*. 05.011.AB.01030.01   CD1-95

Common Nightingale *Luscinia megarhynchos*, Bou Hedma, Tunisia, 4 May 2005 *(René Pop)*

Jackie and Nick Hull are two regulars at Poole's bird pub. Early one spring, I told them where I had heard a Garden Warbler *S borin* singing deep in some undergrowth. Seeing myself as a bit of a whiz on bird sounds, it was pretty embarrassing when at the next pub evening Nick told everyone that it had turned out to be a Blackcap *S atricapilla*. In England this mistake is frequently made, but why? And why, in my case, could I consistently identify Garden Warbler song and once even managed it from the open window of a speeding car, and yet made this kind of mistake with Blackcap. Curious, I started to ask every birder I met how they separate the songs of Garden Warbler and Blackcap. Some answers were best summed up by Percy Edwards' description of the Garden Warbler taking singing lessons from a brook passing under a small bridge, and his comparison of Blackcap to Pan running his bearded lips over his seven pipes before bounding through the woods. Svensson, ever the poet in the *Collins bird guide*, had described Blackcap "turning into clear melancholy flute notes at the end".

A few of my experts joined Percy and Lars and identified the Blackcap songs by timbre. "Garden Warbler has a mellower, blackbird-like timbre" said Magnus for example. Others used pitch: "Garden Warbler constantly drops into the lower notes while Blackcap reaches for the higher", but most used the length of the song "Garden Warbler sings appreciably longer songs than Blackcap". One thing I noticed in probing was that Scandinavian birders did not see the Blackcap/Garden Warbler conundrum as much of a challenge at all.

This gave me a clue and I started to realise that, as with migrant warblers in North America, many of the Blackcaps we hear in Britain and southern and western Europe in the early spring are wintering birds or are still *en route*, so when we hear these migrants they are singing subsong or plastic song or a mixture of both.

In Poole Harbour where the mistake was made, Blackcaps winter in gardens in reasonable numbers, and ringing recoveries have shown that in late March and early April they leave to breed in Belgium and Germany. Meanwhile other migrant Blackcaps pass through the area from Africa, singing as they go. Simultaneously our local breeding birds arrive and set up territory. Garden Warbler, on the other hand, winters in Africa and is a less common spring migrant and much rarer breeder.

As a consequence, the picture for Blackcaps as they move through parts of Europe is complex, for as they travel they also develop through the full range of songs, crystallising their songs when reaching the breeding grounds. Meanwhile, the Garden Warblers singing the songs I identified from speeding cars are African migrants that have arrived directly at their breeding grounds, singing nearly crystallised songs.

As described by Thorpe, subsong and plastic songs, timbre, prevalent pitch and length of the song phrases are wonderfully varied, making it impossible to use any of the normal identification criteria. Here as a guide are three different stages in the development of Blackcap song. Then these are compared with crystallised Garden Warbler songs.

One of the problems of recording subsongs is seeing the bird, as subsongs are normally performed by birds hidden deep in a bush. Magnus didn't see the bird he was recording (**CD1-96**) and it's one of very few tracks in this guide where the bird hasn't been visually identified. Still, he did see a Blackcap subsequently and I

CD1-96   **Blackcap** *Sylvia atricapilla* IJmuiden, Noord-Holland, Netherlands, 5 September 2004. Subsong of a first-winter during autumn migration. Background: Common Chiffchaff *Phylloscopus collybita* and Western Jackdaw *Corvus monedula*. 04.040.MR.13840.11

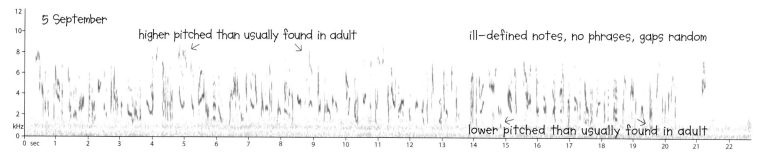

CD1-97   **Blackcap** *Sylvia atricapilla* Monte Gordo, São Nicolau, Cape Verde Islands, 16 February 2004. Near-continuous plastic song. Background: distant village sounds. 04.004.MR.04138.11

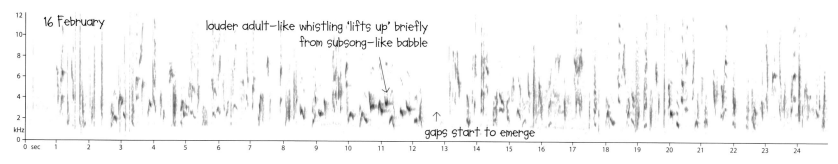

CD1-98   **Blackcap** *Sylvia atricapilla* Longbredy, Dorset, England, 3 June 2001. Crystallised song of an adult male in June. Background: Common Wood Pigeon *Columba palumbus*, Winter Wren *Troglodytes troglodytes*, Dunnock *Prunella modularis*, Western Jackdaw *Corvus monedula*, Rook *Corvus frugilegus* and Common Chaffinch *Fringilla coelebs*. 01.011.MC.00700.10

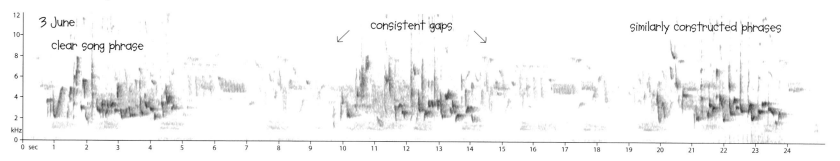

CD1-99   **Garden Warbler** *Sylvia borin* Posterholt, Limburg, Netherlands, 07:52, 2 May 2000. Crystallised song of an adult, presumed male. Background: Eurasian Collared Dove *Streptopelia decaocto*, Common Chiffchaff *Phylloscopus collybita* and Common Chaffinch *Fringilla coelebs*. 00.004.ΛB.12759.00

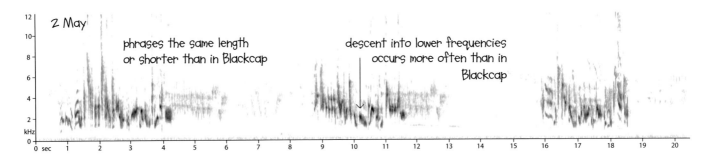

can vouch for it sounding just like the 10 or so Blackcaps that winter in my garden and entertain me by singing subsongs out of sight all through the early spring. Again this subsong is quieter than the 'normal' song, with a different pattern of notes, and the bird stops to call for a period in the middle. It is difficult to catch any mimicry but that doesn't mean it's not there. The song bursts are longer, and the frequency range varies more than in the full song. Although it is difficult to prove, this subsong has characteristics that suggest that it was sung by a female, for example the 'weeping' call (cf Bergmann & Helb 1982).

As Blackcap songs crystallise they go through several stages, and this next recording is an example of plastic song or possibly even what Marler & Slabbekoorn (2004) call early plastic song **(CD1-97)**. You can hear the crystallisation process in action as a loud whistled adult-like phrase emerges from the chatter of the subsong after 10 seconds. There are hardly any gaps in the song, which lacks clear phrasing, and much of the time it strongly resembles subsong.

In studies of song development the full crystallisation of song seems to happen suddenly, and this final Blackcap example **(CD1-98)** is a full song recorded in an idyllic thatched cottage garden in the heart of Dorset. We have also included the song of an adult Garden Warbler for you to compare these Blackcap songs with **(CD1-99)**.

Another *Sylvia* warbler that sings as it migrates is Lesser Whitethroat and in Dorset, towards the end of April, I pointed out a singing but hidden one to my wife, Mo. On returning home, I wanted to show her the ease of using The Sound Approach database. I looked up and played an example of a Lesser Whitethroat song from our collection **(CD2-01)**. When she didn't recognise the bird in the recording I then found another recording made in late April of an early plastic song, the intermediate stage between subsong and plastic song **(CD2-02)**, which she immediately recognised as the song she had heard that morning.

CD2-01 **Lesser Whitethroat** *Sylvia curruca* Kuligi, Biebrza valley, Podłaskie, Poland, 11:00, 12 May 2005. Territorial song dominated by rattles, recorded in Marek Borkowski's garden. This bird had arrived five days earlier and was apparently still unmated. Background: Common Cuckoo *Cuculus canorus*, Wood Lark *Lullula arborea*, White Wagtail *Motacilla alba*, Garden Warbler *Sylvia borin*, Common Chiffchaff *Phylloscopus collybita*, Spotted Flycatcher *Muscicapa striata*, Common Chaffinch *Fringilla coelebs* and European Fire-bellied Toad *Bombina bombina*. 05.011.MR.01540.00

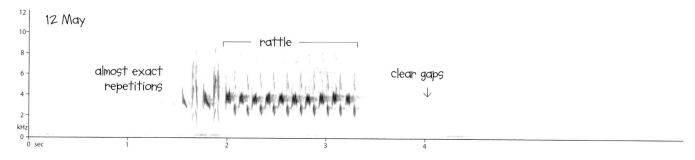

CD2-02 **Lesser Whitethroat** *Sylvia curruca* Texel, Noord-Holland, Netherlands, 25 April 2003. Plastic song of a spring migrant, a presumed first-year male. Background: Greylag Goose *Anser anser*, Common Pheasant *Phasianus colchicus*, Lesser Black-backed Gull *Larus fuscus*, Sandwich Tern *Sterna sandvicensis*, Winter Wren *Troglodytes troglodytes*, Dunnock *Prunella modularis*, Sedge Warbler *Acrocephalus schoenobaenus* and Willow Warbler *Phylloscopus trochilus*. 03.012.MR.10007.11

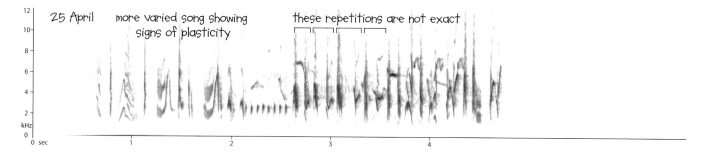

I had mentioned in my original paper (Constantine 1994) that while you are attempting to learn calls and songs, so too are some of the birds you are listening to. What I hadn't mentioned is that in order to compare, you should always rely on referenced recordings where the date and location are given. This increases the chances of you comparing birds of the same age and stage in song development. Papers on bird identification have been doing this with photographs for years, but it also has to become general practice in discussions about sounds.

An awareness of plastic song is important when identifying spring rarities, many of which are first-year birds. In species where first-year males normally return to where they hatched, songs of vagrants are likely to be immature; a vagrant is by definition outside of its normal breeding range, so it won't have the benefit of feedback from other males to help crystallise its song. On the 23rd of May 1994, Alan McCall found a warbler in the Kergold plantation in Shetland and he thought that it could be a Marsh Warbler. The next day another birder thought it was a '*Hippolais*' warbler, then the concensus later swung back to it being a Marsh Warbler. On the 26th of May, Bill Jackson recorded it. It was singing a plastic song or as Bill put it "quiet much slower melodic and fluty". It was eventually identified as a Blyth's Reed

Warbler. He asked me at the time to analyse the songs, which I did without reference material. Now thanks to The Sound Approach we can compare the two species at this stage in their development. Plastic song of spring migrant Blyth's Reed **(CD2-03)** can be much faster and more varied than fully mature song heard on a breeding territory. As we have learnt this could lead to misidentification as Marsh Warbler, whose plastic song is faster and more complex at this stage in its development **(CD2-04)**.

CD2-03   **Blyth's Reed Warbler** *Acrocephalus dumetorum* Chokpak Station, Kokshetau Oblast, Kazakhstan, 2 May 2000. Plastic song of a spring migrant, presumably a bird less than one year old. Crystallised song of an adult can be heard in CD2-41. Background: Carrion Crow *Corvus corone orientalis*. 00.020.MR.00720.00

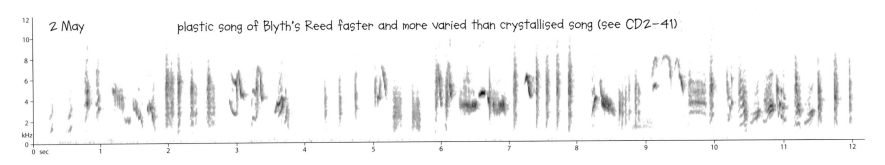

CD2-04   **Marsh Warbler** *Acrocephalus palustris* Göksu delta, Mersin, Turkey, 15 May 2001. Plastic song of a spring migrant. Crystallised song of an adult can be heard in CD2-38. Background: Crested Lark *Galerida cristata*, Graceful Prinia *Prinia gracilis* and European Reed Warbler *Acrocephalus scirpaceus fuscus*. 01.019.MR.11650.00

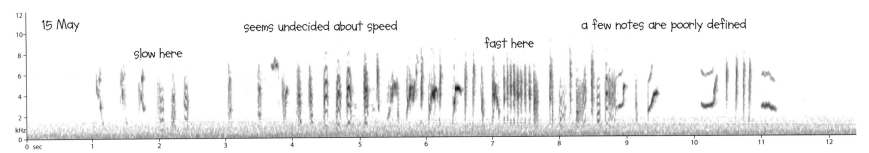

Not everything young sounds so different. Fan-tailed Warblers are capable of producing a very adult sounding song at a very early age. Every summer in the south-western Netherlands, from early July onwards, Zitting Cisticolas *Cisticola juncidis* turn up and start to sing as they set up new territories **(CD2-05)**. These are thought to be juveniles dispersing from the nearest regular breeding grounds in western France (van den Berg & Bosman 2001). Given the very short time they have before claiming their own territories, it is not surprising that the song of these birds is

slightly higher pitched and sharper. This difference is also noticeable when the birds first sing in the spring.

I have to admit that once Shaun Robson, another Poole birder, had got the idea of song plasticity he did start to find birds singing these songs. I was a little gripped when he heard what must have been a juvenile Common Grasshopper Warbler because I had always wondered whether a juvenile Common Grasshopper or Savi's Warbler could be mistaken for each other. I was thrilled when we recorded this juvenile Savi's **(CD2-06)** and this juvenile Common Grasshopper **(CD2-07)** singing in mid-August. Common Grasshoppers also produce a 'wobbly' kind of plastic song **(CD2-08)** and it can sound like a different *Locustella* species; maybe a little like Lanceolated Warbler.

CD2-05   **Zitting Cisticola** *Cisticola juncidis* Noord-Beveland, Zeeland, Netherlands, 27 July 2002. Song of a juvenile male in the Netherlands in late July. Background: Barn Swallow *Hirundo rustica*, European Reed Warbler *Acrocephalus scirpaceus* and Common Reed Bunting *Emberiza schoeniclus*. 02.036.MR.02027.01

CD2-06   **Savi's Warbler** *Locustella luscinioides* Zwarte Meer, Overijssel, Netherlands, 07:30, 21 August 2005. Subsong of a juvenile, with *plik* calls of a second individual. Background: Gadwall *Anas strepera*, Eurasian Coot *Fulica atra*, Common Gull *Larus canus*, Common Chiffchaff *Phylloscopus collybita*, Great Tit *Parus major* and European Blue Tit *Cyanistes caeruleus*. 05.024.MR.04513.32

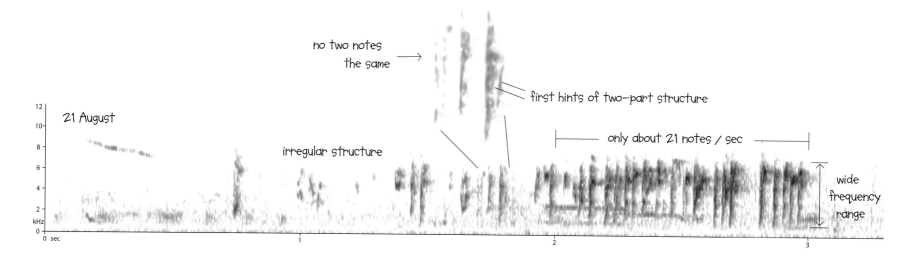

21 August

no two notes the same →

first hints of two-part structure

irregular structure

only about 21 notes / sec

wide frequency range

See CD1-04: **Savi's Warbler** *Locustella luscinioides* crystallised song

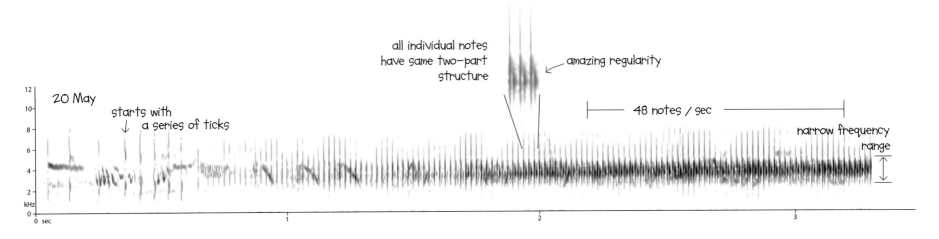

20 May

starts with
↓ a series of ticks

all individual notes
have same two-part
structure

← amazing regularity

48 notes / sec

narrow frequency
range

CD2-07 **Common Grasshopper Warbler** *Locustella naevia* IJmuiden, Noord-Holland, Netherlands, 06:30, 17 August 2005. Subsong of a juvenile. Background: Herring Gull *Larus argentatus* and Lesser Black-backed Gull *Larus fuscus*. 05.023.MR.02405.01

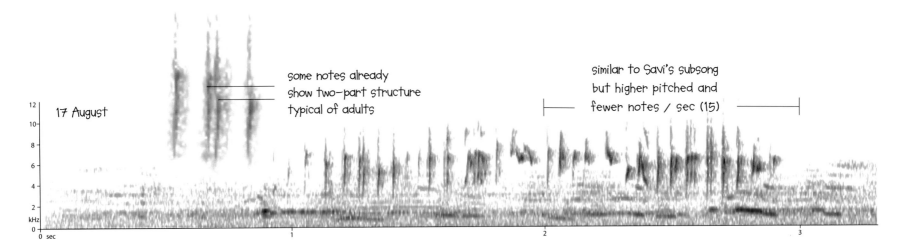

17 August

some notes already
show two-part structure
typical of adults

similar to Savi's subsong
but higher pitched and
fewer notes / sec (15)

CD2-08 **Common Grasshopper Warbler** *Locustella naevia* Kuligi, Biebrza valley, Podłaskie, Poland, 06:45, 14 May 2005. Plastic song, perhaps a first-year male still on migration. Background: Common Snipe *Gallinago gallinago*, Eurasian Skylark *Alauda arvensis*, Thrush Nightingale *Luscinia luscinia* and Yellowhammer *Emberiza citrinella*. 05.011.MR.04749.00

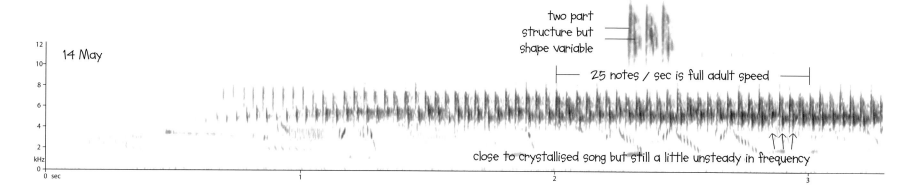

14 May

two part structure but shape variable

25 notes / sec is full adult speed

close to crystallised song but still a little unsteady in frequency

See CD1-03: **Common Grasshopper Warbler** *Locustella naevia* crystallised song

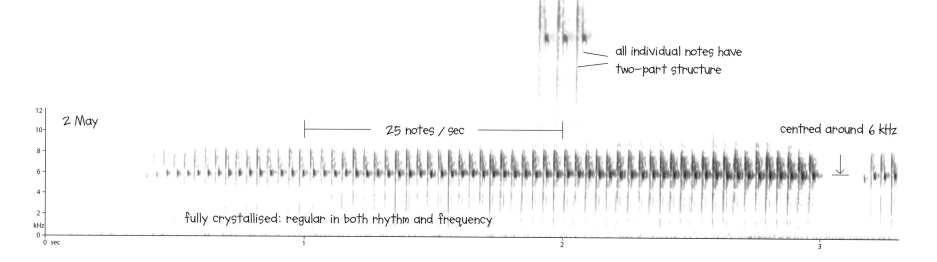

2 May

all individual notes have two-part structure

25 notes / sec

centred around 6 kHz

fully crystallised: regular in both rhythm and frequency

Go to the right habitat on a calm morning in late summer, especially when migrants are passing through, and you will have a good chance of hearing subsongs. They are very pertinent in the identification of *Phylloscopus* warblers. By sound, an increasing number of Siberian *Phylloscopus* warblers are being found wintering in western Europe, although you could doubt your ears if you had listened to commercial recordings of adults on the breeding grounds. For many of the rarer 'phylloscs', breeding as far away as Siberia, these are the only kinds of songs

we are likely to hear from them. Listen to this Yellow-browed Warbler subsong recorded in late September (**CD2-09**). The date alone would suggest that this is what you would hear, and only the first hints of adult song are starting to emerge. As another example listen to a recording of plastic song of a Pallas's Leaf Warbler recorded in early April near Rotterdam, the Netherlands (**CD2-10**). Again the date and place would lead one to expect plastic song and it sounds as if the bird is ready to crystallise its song in competition with other males. However, a vagrant like

CD2-09   **Yellow-browed Warbler** *Phylloscopus inornatus* IJmuiden, Noord-Holland, Netherlands, 11:30, 22 September 2005. Subsong of a first-winter, most adult-like towards the end when it sings three-note songs. Background: Common Chiffchaff *Phylloscopus collybita*, dog-walkers, flies and rustling poplar leaves. 05.026.MR.03513.11

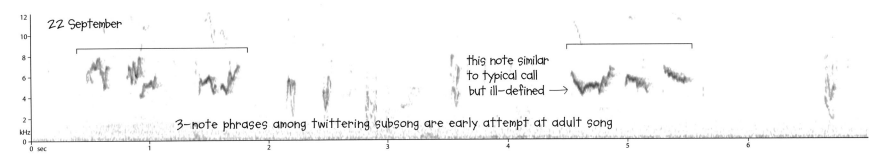

CD2-10   **Pallas's Leaf Warbler** *Phylloscopus proregulus* Vlaardingen, Zuid-Holland, Netherlands, 13:10, 1 April 2002. Plastic song of a presumed first-year male. Background: Common Chiffchaff *Phylloscopus collybita*, Great Tit *Parus major* and suburbia. 01.002.AB.03623b.11

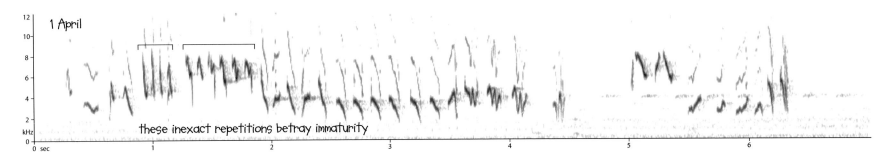

this may never have the crystallising opportunity and could stay at this stage throughout the spring, or develop some kind of mixed song.

Common Chiffchaffs are usually the only *Phylloscopus* warblers to be found in winter in Europe, but every year a few Siberian Chiffchaffs are discovered among them. Given the difficulties of separating Siberians from other chiffchaffs on plumage, it is useful to be able to recognise not only their calls (**CD1-15**) but

also the kinds of songs they may give from autumn through to spring. Listen to a spring migrant Magnus recorded in Almaty, Kazakhstan, on the 16th of May. He captured this bird in the final stages of crystallisation and in the first recording it is singing plastic song, usefully littered with call notes (**CD2-11**). In the second cut you can hear how its song is structured. It now sounds much as a Siberian Chiffchaff will sing upon reaching its breeding grounds further north, still frozen as this bird sings in May (**CD2-12**).

CD2-11   **Siberian Chiffchaff** *Phylloscopus collybita tristis* Gorky Park, Almaty, Kazakhstan, 16 May 2003. Plastic song of a spring migrant, incorporating call notes. Background: Eurasian Collared Dove *Streptopelia decaocto*, Common Blackbird *Turdus merula*, Great Tit *Parus major* and Eurasian Magpie *Pica pica*. 03.013.MR.14759.02

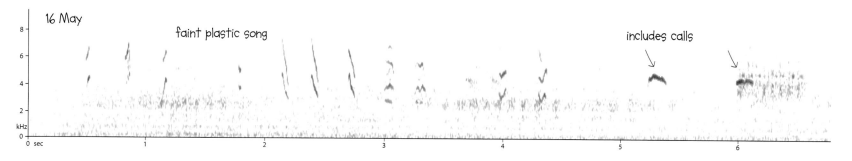

CD2-12   **Siberian Chiffchaff** *Phylloscopus collybita tristis* Gorky Park, Almaty, Kazakhstan, 16 May 2003. More crystallised song of the same spring migrant. Background: Eurasian Collared Dove *Streptopelia decaocto*, Golden Oriole *Oriolus oriolus*, Hume's Leaf Warbler *Phylloscopus humei*, Great Tit *Parus major* and singing Eurasian Magpie *Pica pica*. 03.013.MR.14605.01

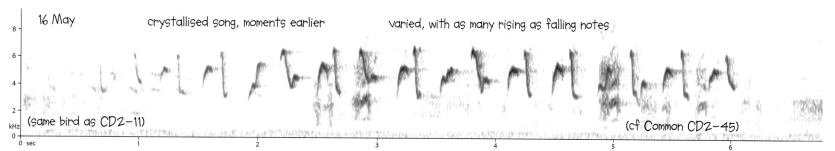

Unlike many songbirds, which mimic other birds more in their subsongs than in their adult songs, Marsh Warbler does this less in its subsong **(CD2-13)**. Luckily, even at this very early stage the difference in tempo between this song and that of European Reed Warblers (CD2-40) is already apparent, Marsh having the faster and more varied song. The European Reed's subsong in **CD2-14** is much more like the adults' crystallised song.

Sometimes it can be hard to separate the songs of Common Blackbird and Mistle Thrush *T viscivorus*. At the beginning of the season, when their songs first start to crystallise, blackbirds sing simpler songs than later. In areas where they are partial migrants, some stay to winter in towns and are in position to breed early in the season. In the towns, it is warmer, there is plenty of food, and population densities can be very high. As the weeks pass and competition increases, the songs of blackbirds breeding at higher densities become more complex and easier to separate

CD2-13   **Marsh Warbler** *Acrocephalus palustris* Polder Achteraf, Nieuw Loosdrecht, Noord-Holland, Netherlands, 06:00, 7 August 2005. Fairly loud subsong of a juvenile, almost certainly in the territory where it hatched. Background: Eurasian Coot *Fulica atra*. 05.020.MR.05928.12

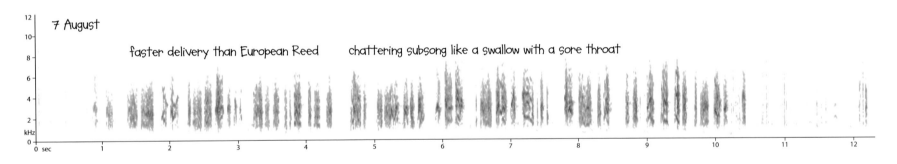

CD2-14   **European Reed Warbler** *Acrocephalus scirpaceus* IJmuiden, Noord-Holland, Netherlands, 13 September 2002. Subsong of a juvenile, possibly a migrant. Background: Dunnock *Prunella modularis* Common Chiffchaff *Phylloscopus collybita* and Great Tit *Parus major*. 02.040.MR.13345.01

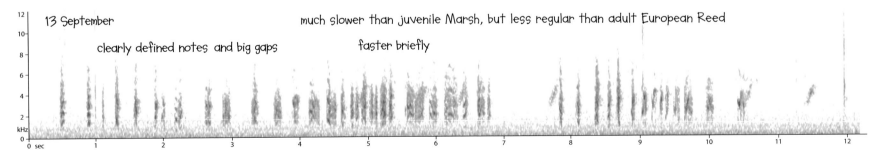

from Mistle. Those blackbirds that flew south for the winter return to breed when their urban relatives' breeding season is well underway. Sometimes these birds choose traditional rural sites where they breed at much lower densities. There is not as much competitive pressure to enrich their repertoires as there is in town, and consequently the songs of these forest blackbirds remain simpler throughout the breeding season. The situation is similar for Mistle Thrush: listen to one which I recorded from the back of a frozen Finnish chalet where it had only just arrived. The majority of Mistle here were still in flocks foraging along the frozen tracks, and this song had to be edited to remove the sounds of Dick singing as he ran out of the sauna and into the snowy air (CD2-15). Now compare it with one at an earlier date but a later stage in a much longer breeding season in Scotland where Magnus was thinking more of warm porridge than saunas (CD2-16).

CD2-15   **Mistle Thrush** *Turdus viscivorus* Syöte, Pudas Järvi, Lapland, Finland, 19:00, 8 May 2005. Simple song with fragments of quieter plastic song; a bird that had just arrived to find its breeding grounds still in winter conditions. Background: Black Grouse *Tetrao tetrix* and Song Thrush *T philomelos*. 05.010.MC.04538a.12

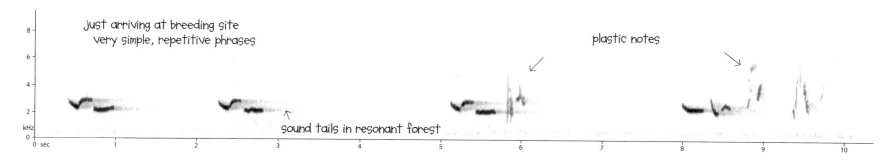

CD2-16   **Mistle Thrush** *Turdus viscivorus* Ardgay, Sutherland, Scotland, 20 March 2002. Longer songs of a bird further on in its breeding season. Background: Meadow Pipit *Anthus pratensis*. 02.010.MR.05713.00

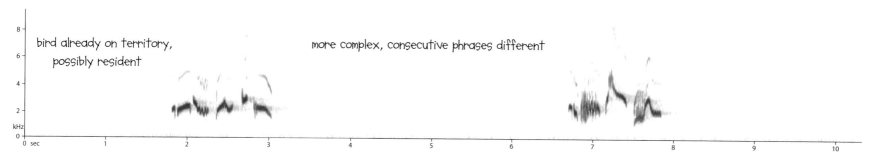

Part 6: Sex, seduction and jumping the neighbour's wife

Sexing sounds, and strategies for mates and rivals

I remember reading a beautiful introduction to bird sound in *The handbook of birds of the world* 6 by Baptista & Kroodsma (2001), when suddenly I learnt that female Alpine Accentors *P collaris* sing to attract males. I had recorded the song of this species in the French Pyrenees and not imagined that it was anything other than a male. Later, on recounting the story to veteran Dutch birder, Gerald Oreel, he said, "you do realise Dunnock is the same?". It is always easy to disregard female sounds, and most of the time it is assumed that a singing bird is a male. However, **as research continues, more and more female songs are being discovered.** In addition, the repertoires of many species include calls that are exclusive to one sex or the other.

Ducks are not only an excellent example of one of the more sexually dimorphic groups in plumage but also in sounds, with drakes generally having the more 'colourful' and exotic vocal displays. One of my regular Poole bird pub companions, Shaun Robson, is a wise commentator on all aspects of my quest to understand bird sounds. He is sometimes pushed to the limits of his patience with my constant questions. This was best summed up when a calling female Mallard flew past and I asked if he had ever thought about the sounds made by female American Black Duck *A rubripes*. "I don't know and I don't want to know" was the sanguine reply. Let's start with Shaun's male and female Mallard

and how to tell them apart. Although Mallard have a variety of different calls, males and females always have quite different sounding voices (**CD2-17**). One of the main calls of male Mallard is often preceded by a quiet ticking sound. Females have much louder calls; their sound is a much fuller and rounder quacking, using a far wider range of frequencies. American Black Duck's corresponding sounds aren't so different so Shaun may well have made the right decision.

Mallard *Anas platyrhynchos* Weerribben, Overijssel, Netherlands, 28 March 2003. Typical calls of a **male** as it swam past the microphone at night. Each call is preceded by a quiet clicking sound. Background: Greylag Goose *Anser anser* and Greater White-fronted Goose *A albifrons*. 04.010.MR.05545.01   **CD2-17a** 0:00-0:22

Mallard *Anas platyrhynchos* Kollumerpomp, Friesland, Netherlands, 01:13, 17 March 2003. Typical quacking of a **female**; a much quieter male can be heard after about her 10th quack. Background: Eurasian Coot *Fulica atra*. 03.003.AB.13859.00   **CD2-17b** 0:23-0:51

Shaun Robson at Poole, Dorset, 20 April 2006 (*Arnoud B van den Berg*)

Madeiran Storm-petrel *Oceanodroma castro* cold-season type, Farilhão Grande, Berlengas, Leiria, Portugal, 22 September 2003 (*Magnus Robb*). At same site as the birds on CD2-24.

Hamish, Shaun and I make up a winning local bird race team in Dorset, aided and abetted by ace bird race driver Nick Hopper. A good team needs a mix of skills and if you want quacking ducks identified in the dark, Nick is your man. Nick is able to pick off female Common Teal *A crecca* by sound at 05:00 am on a winter's morning, then drive at such speed, that as he advises Shaun on the fine detail of identifying duck sound, Shaun's too busy holding on to comment. Try for yourself, pop this CD in the car stereo, put your foot down and listen to a female Common Teal recorded by Killian on a spring night in Lapland (**CD2-18**). Her quacks are shorter, higher-pitched and weaker than the corresponding quacks of female Mallard. After about 12 seconds a male can be heard, giving very different short whistled calls as he approaches and settles on the water; the female becomes excited and calls more loudly.

CD2-18 **Common Teal** *Anas crecca* Lake Toranki, Kuusamo, Lapland, Finland, 01:30, 16 May 2003. Quiet quacking of a female, becoming louder when a male arrives giving short whistled calls. Background: Black Grouse *Tetrao tetrix*, Red-necked Grebe *Podiceps grisegena*, Wood Sandpiper *Tringa glareola*, Song Thrush *Turdus philomelos* and Redwing *T iliacus*. 03.006.KM.05215.11

Listen to two pairs of King Eiders *S spectabilis* as they swam past a microphone Magnus had laid beside a tundra pool in the Lena delta, Siberia (**CD2-19**). The females are only responsible for the rather nondescript *gog-gog-gog* sounds, while the males produce a range of beautiful crooning sounds that differ from those of Common Eider in that they are delivered more rapidly and with a slight vibrato.

King Eider *Somateria spectabilis* Nizhny Bobrowsky island, Lena delta, Yakutia, Russia, 17:00, 25 June 2004. Two pairs swim past the microphone on a long, narrow pool on the tundra. The more expressive sounds are the males, while the females give *gog-gog-gog* calls hardly differing from female Common Eider calls. Background: Temminck's Stint *Calidris temminckii* and Lapland Longspur *Calcarius lapponicus*. 04.032.MR.20245.01 **CD2-19**

Ruddy Ducks *Oxyura jamaicensis* have a most entertaining display, and these were recorded communally displaying on a lake in the prairies in Alberta, Canada, among a host of other fantastic singing and displaying birds (**CD2-20**). The continuous high peeping sound heard more or less throughout the recording (about three or four per second) is a female Ruddy. Meanwhile, males can be heard giving two different displays. A popping rattle always accompanied by a splash is part of a display called the *ringing rush*, best heard after seven seconds. Incredibly, the popping is produced by the male's feet hitting the water. The other is called the *bubbling* display which you can hear from the start throughout the recording.

Ruddy Duck *Oxyura jamaicensis* Frank Lake, Alberta, Canada, 08:26, 9 June 2003. Male *bubbling* displays (each ending with a quiet *burp*) from start, and *ringing rush* (popping rattle with splash) at for instance 0:07, with continuous peeping of females. Background: American Bittern *Botaurus lentiginosus*, American Coot *Fulica americana*, Franklin's Gull *Larus pipixcan* and Yellow-headed Blackbird *Xanthocephalus xanthocephalus*. 03.024.AB.11500.00 **CD2-20**

Ruddy Ducks *Oxyura jamaicensis*, males in display (right) and females (left), Frank Lake, Alberta, Canada, 9 June 2003 *(Arnoud B van den Berg)*. Same birds as on CD2-20.

It wasn't easy to get Magnus enthusiastic about sexing bird sounds until he found a new example in Siberia in June 2004. On the breeding grounds, Pectoral Sandpipers *C melanotos* are easily sexed; the males are larger, and have an inflatable throat sac that they use to produce their incredible booming song. In this display flight (**CD2-21**) a male is chasing a female and the high, metallic-sounding *krrr krrr* calls heard from the start are produced by the female while the deep *poo-poo-poo-poo…* song is produced by a male, using its throat sac as a resonator. A second male joins the chase at 0:19, making deep churring sounds and male-type flight calls. During the breeding season, the most common calls of males and females, used in all kinds of flight situations including when flushed, can be separated easily (**CD2-22**). Magnus was hooked once he recorded two migrant adult Pectorals together in the Netherlands in mid-July, a few weeks after his Siberian trip, and found that they could still be sexed when they gave the deeper, more snipe-like male calls.

Pectoral Sandpiper *Calidris melanotos*, female, Safety Sound, Seward Peninsula, Alaska, USA, 31 May 2004 *(René Pop)*. Same bird as on CD2-22b.

As you've probably realised Magnus has been something of a work horse throughout this project and sometimes when we started The Sound Approach, we debated skipping certain

CD2-21 **Pectoral Sandpiper** *Calidris melanotos* Lena delta, Yakutia, Russia, 14 June 2004. Background: Little Stint *C minuta* and Curlew Sandpiper *C ferruginea*. 04.028.MR.05546.22

CD2-22a
0:00-0:05 **Pectoral Sandpiper** *Calidris melanotos* Lena delta, Yakutia, Russia, 10 June 2004. Two loud snipe-like calls of a male in flight. Background: Curlew Sandpiper *C ferruginea*. 04.026.MR.13638.01

Pectoral Sandpiper *Calidris melanotos* Safety Sound, Seward Peninsula, Alaska, USA, 19:45, 31 May 2004. Call of a flushed female. Background: Lapland Longspur *Calcarius lapponicus*. 04.011.AB.04654.02 **CD2-22b**
0:06-0:11

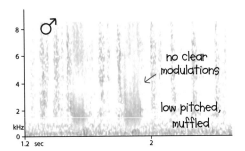

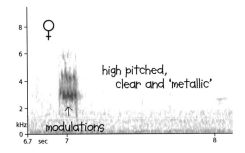

Cory's Shearwater *Calonectris borealis* Barranco del Infierno, Tenerife, Canary Islands, 8 April 2001. Shearwaters calling as they fly around in a narrow canyon a couple of hours after sunset. 01.009.MR.00635.00

species like the shearwaters, because nobody ever hears them, and Magnus's time and our money probably didn't allow. Nonetheless we couldn't resist and yet again we sent in Magnus, this time to visit a Cory's Shearwater *Calonectris borealis* colony on Tenerife, Canary Islands. When I heard the recordings he made in Barranco del Infierno, or 'canyon of hell', I was glad if a little jealous (**CD2-23**). He had to wait what seemed a very long time after sunset, and had been on the point of leaving when the first birds started to call. After a while, the amazing acoustics of the very steep-sided canyon were echoing to the sound of shearwaters swarming in the darkness. Shearwaters call to form and maintain pair bonds, having to identify their male or female in the dark. Male and female calls are very easy to tell apart

(Ristow & Wink 1979). As with most shearwaters, female Cory's have deeper, coarser voices than males. You can hear one passing close by several times, coming closest at 0:28.

Sexing Madeiran Storm-petrels *Oceanodroma castro* vocally was first described by Paul James & Hugh Robertson (1985). They described three calls 'high, burrow and flight'. As is the way with such descriptions they become embarrassing, and so it is here with 'flight' being heard both in flight and in the burrow (**CD2-24**). The 'high' call, a high squealing heard at the start of the recording, is the same in both sexes. In the other two calls, the 'burrow' call and the 'chatter' call, males and females can be told apart. As in Cory's Shearwater, females have the coarser, less melodious voice, and in Madeiran Storm-petrel this shows in a sonagram as a solid dark vertical smudge over their frequency range, while males have a more melodious voice, showing clear harmonic bands. The first 'flight' calls to be heard clearly, at 0:19

Madeiran Storm-petrel *Oceanodroma castro* cold-season type Farilhão Grande, Berlengas islands, Leiria, Portugal, around midnight, 22 September 2003. Calls by two or three males and three females. These birds belong to the cold-season breeding population of this species. In some parts of the North Atlantic, a hot-season population with different biometrics uses the same burrows in late spring and summer (Sangster 1999). The two populations also sound different, and everything points towards them being separate species, but they have yet to be described formally. 03.036.MR.10333a.01

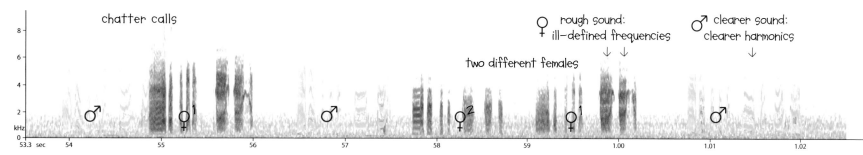

and 0:28, are of a female. A male's 'burrow' calls are heard throughout the recording until 0:53 seconds, at which point you can hear a nine second sequence of 'flight' calls of a male and two females calling to each other.

Having done a lot of my spring birding in Mallorca I had heard European Scops Owls *Otus scops* many times but only learnt that they duet while searching for a Spotted Crake *P porzana* with a Belgian bird tour leader, who pointed it out. In duetting song the female responds to the male with a slightly higher-pitched song, often slightly 'out of sync' with the male. In this recording (**CD2-25**), listen to a pair performing a duet.

Common Swifts have calls that can also be sexed. One of their most characteristic sounds is duetting, heard most often at dusk, in which a rapid series of short screams is given by the two in alternation (**CD2-26**). Erich Kaiser (1997) discovered that in these duets, the higher *swee* is always given by a female and the lower

Common Swift *Apus apus* Ishak Pasha palace, Ağrı, Turkey, 5 June 2002. Duetting at dusk; a pair already in their nest respond to another swift that is still airborne. Background: visitors to the ruined palace. 02.032.MR.12443.01   **CD2-26**

Pallid Swift *Apus pallidus* Islote de Benidorm, País Valenciano, Spain, dusk, 7 August 2002. At least two duetting pairs calling from their nests at dusk. Background: Yellow-legged Gull *Larus michahellis*. 02.038.MR.00921.00   **CD2-27**

ree is always a male. In our recordings, a similar alternation of high and low screams suggests that the same rule applies with duetting Pallid Swift (**CD2-27**). The sounds are differently inflected from those of Common Swift, as you can see in the sonagrams.

CD2-25   **European Scops Owl** *Otus scops* Pollensa, Mallorca, Spain, 06:00, 9 April 2002. Song duet, with male being louder, lower-pitched bird and female weaker (or more distant) and higher-pitched. Background: other scops owls. 02.008.MC.01842.02

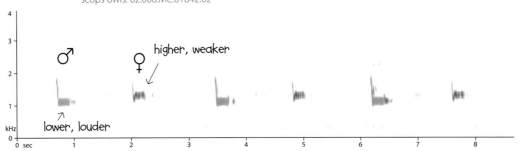

European Scops Owl *Otus scops*, Mallorca, Spain, 28 April 1986 *(Killian Mullarney)*

Ultra-crystallised songs

The song that the male Collared Flycatcher *F albicollis* uses to attract a mate to a nest hole is not very exciting to you and I, but Magnus loved it **(CD2-28)**. Having heard it I sort of dismissed it as just a subsong and he exploded. "It is not just a subsong. Its highly motivated, sexually charged and ultra-crystallised."

It is a fact that we listen to and interpret bird songs from our own perspective and just because a bird song is not easily audible to us it doesn't mean that it isn't important to them.

Collared Flycatcher *Ficedula albicollis*, adult male, Noord-Ginkel, Ede, Gelderland, Netherlands, 11 June 2006 *(Roland Jansen)*

CD2-28 **Collared Flycatcher** *Ficedula albicollis* Białowieza forest, Podłaskie, Poland, 07:45, 6 May 2005. Quiet, imitative song of a first-summer male trying three times to tempt a female into a nest cavity he has selected. Background: Common Chiffchaff *Phylloscopus collybita*, Wood Warbler *P sibilatrix*, Great Tit *Parus major* and Common Chaffinch *Fringilla coelebs*. 05.007.MR.02045.02

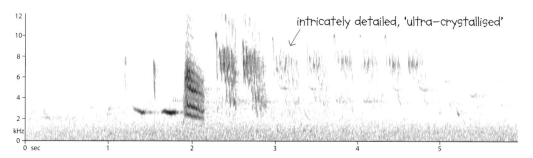

Males of many species reserve their finest songs for the time when their seductive powers need to be at their height – immediately prior to copulation. Listen to what happens when this Western Orphean Warbler *S hortensis*, which has been patiently singing its simple, territorial song for the first 15 seconds, sees a female nearby **(CD2-29)**. Suddenly he changes to a quieter but much longer and more intricately detailed one as he pursues her.

CD2-29 **Western Orphean Warbler** *Sylvia hortensis* Torrejón El Rubio, Tahéna, Extremadura, Spain, 12:00, 27 April 2004. Simple song for 15 sec, then complex courtship song as a female arrives. Background: European Blue Tit *Cyanistes caeruleus*, Great Tit *Parus major* and Corn Bunting *Emberiza calandra*. 04.010.MC.04345.12

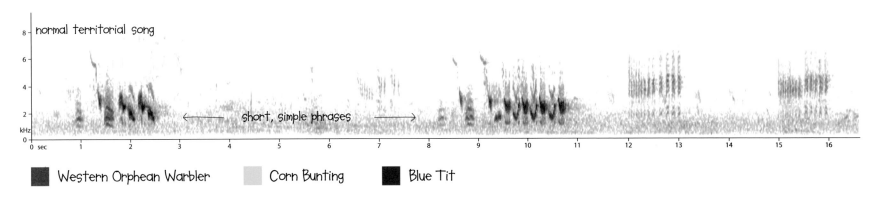

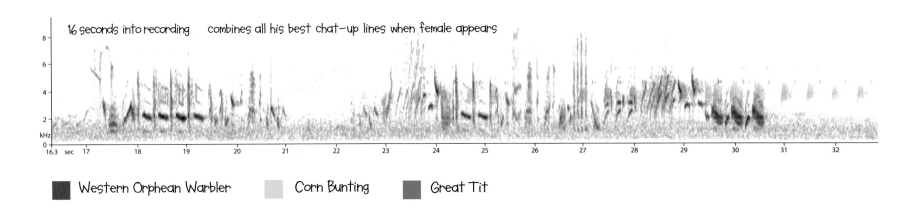

CD2-30   **Desert Wheatear** *Oenanthe deserti* Douz, Kebili, Tunisia, 11:22, 6 May 2005. Ecstatic songs of three males in dispute at their territorial borders in a sand desert. 05.008.AB.12014.01

This kind of ecstatic songs are also used by some species in other highly charged situations, such as territorial disputes. Listen to these three male Desert Wheatears *Oenanthe deserti* recorded in Tunisia (**CD2-30**), singing with unusual virtuosity in a territorial conflict. The songs heard at the end of the recording are closer to the normal territory-marking song. An example from closer to home can be heard in a recording of Common Blackbird ecstatic song (**CD2-31**), heard during a territorial encounter between two males. One sang this weird song, displaying to the other with writhing threat postures, while the other adopted a submissive posture giving *srrr* 'flight' calls, perhaps as a sign of submission.

Desert Wheatear *Oenanthe deserti*, male, Douz, Kebili, Tunisia, 6 May 2005 *(René Pop)*. One of three males singing in dispute on CD2-30.

CD2-31   **Common Blackbird** *Turdus merula* Amsterdamse Waterleidingduinen, Noord-Holland, Netherlands, 5 March 2002. Rather strangled-sounding quiet and very detailed song of an adult male threatening another male. Background: Great Spotted Woodpecker *Dendrocopos major*, Dunnock *Prunella modularis* and Marsh Tit *Poecile palustris*. 02.008.MR.11840.01

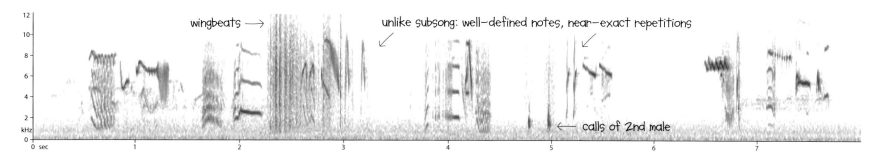

Having given thought to Magnus's point of view I now understand that in dismissing these 'ultra-crystallised' songs as subsongs we miss the point. I think that as The Sound Approach continues we will find that in many species songs are used in this kind of situation which sound closer to subsong or plastic song because of their greater length, lower volume and more varied nature, often including more mimicry. However, there is nothing 'plastic' or undeveloped about them. Rather, they might be seen as an 'ultra-crystallisation' of the subsongs some birds spend so long in the bushes practising until the bird's singing skills have reached their highest level of perfection.

So, the mature song repertoire of adults goes from powerful but stereotyped territorial songs to intricately crystallised and intense pre-copulation songs. Song may be used to attract a mate, and some species use song only for this. Catchpole (Catchpole & Slater 1995) discovered that Sedge Warblers stop singing once paired and may only sing again when the female is on eggs in an attempt to attract a second female. Starlings are the same, and these birds, which are so vocal for much of the year, are often quiet in the peak spring period for song in other species. On the other hand, song may be used primarily to proclaim ownership of a territory, or advertising and territorial songs may be combined.

Great Reed Warbler is a rarity in Dorset, although one took up residence 'just up the road' one spring and sang for three weeks. The song of an unpaired male has a steady, forceful beat like two carpenters taking it in turns to hammer, a big hammer creating low-pitched *dur dur dur* sounds immediately followed by a small one making higher-pitched *dee dee dee* sounds. If it impersonates anything, the feeling you get is that it likes frog and toad sounds, as this is what you could mistake it for in its lower ranges. Song length is also an interesting aspect here, as Catchpole (1983) has found that Great Reed begins the breeding season by singing long varied songs to attract a mate (the more varied the songs the quicker a mate appears), and simplifies this once a pair has been formed, then tending to sing short song phrases. Compare long unpaired song (**CD2-32**) and short paired song of this species (**CD2-33**) for yourself. The latter are so simple they consist of little more than a phrase of low *dur* notes followed by a phrase of high *dee* notes, with slight variations in rhythm each time.

Great Reed Warbler *Acrocephalus arundinaceus* Parc Natural S'Albufera, Mallorca, Spain, 10:15, 19 April 2000. Long songs of a male that arrived a day or two before the recording was made, and was presumably still unpaired. Background: Cetti's Warbler *Cettia cetti* and another Great Reed Warbler in the distance. 00.007.MC.00900.20   **CD2-32**

Great Reed Warbler *Acrocephalus arundinaceus* Reeuwijkse Plassen, Zuid-Holland, Netherlands, 07:42, 14 May 2000. Short songs of a male that was presumably already paired. Background: Black-tailed Godwit *Limosa limosa*, Black-headed Gull *Larus ridibundus*, Eurasian Collared Dove *Streptopelia decaocto*, Sedge Warbler *Acrocephalus schoenobaenus* and Winter Wren *Troglodytes troglodytes*. 03.013.AB.00007.01   **CD2-33**

Song matching: how birds cheat to avoid bringing up another bird's young

Consider the classic, wholesome image of a songbird, singing its heart out to welcome the spring with purity and joy. Science has uncovered a far sleazier truth: singing is actually a kind of poker game where the players are constantly gambling and bluffing. The winners can have their wicked way with another player's 'bird', while the losers bring up another player's young, or in the worst case they die.

One of the most exciting writers about this subject is Eugene Morton, who summed up the singing behaviour of territorial birds as "an evolutionary arms race". The competition starts in spring when songbirds stake out their territories, singing from song posts, or earlier in a non-migratory species. Adults occupy the best territories first, and then when first-year males arrive they fill any gaps. Young birds copy the song phrases of older ones as their songs crystallise; adults already present are their tutors for this last phase of their education. In some species such as Common Blackbirds and Great Tits, older birds may also learn some new sounds, perhaps emulating some phrase by a more successful neighbour.

Degradation, as we have heard, is caused by reverberation and reflections from foliage, rocks and other obstacles however small, and it tends to increase with distance from the sound source. This is the principle means by which songbirds judge the distance to their rivals, and it is one reason why song matching is so important. Morton (1982) explains in his ranging hypothesis: "if the listener has learned to sing his neighbors' songs, he can match this undegraded song stored in his brain to the song he hears. Therefore, if the listener has learned neighbors' songs, he is able to determine more accurately his distance from the singer and therefore challenge the singer if it is near and ignore the singer if it is far away". Morton (1996) later wrote: "A loud song, detectable over a long distance because of high source amplitude, may still be ignored by listening birds if it has become degraded." Similarly, a recording played as a lure by birders may be ignored, no matter how loudly it is played, if crucial parts of the sound are degraded due to having been recorded from too great a distance, or with poor equipment.

Bearing this in mind, it becomes clear why birds always select their song perches so carefully. Their aim is to avoid acoustic degradation and project as far as they can, trying to sound closer than they really are to their neighbours, and increasing the amount of territory they can seem to be present in at any one time. At the same time, optimum sound projection allows them to reach a maximum number of potential mates in the general area. It is cleverer to sing from the ideal perch or trajectory than to spend more energy singing louder. Everything about the choice of perch has this question of degradation in mind and conversely, when still at the subsong stage, singers opt for dense foliage to encourage degradation in order to prevent any aggressive response.

The rather Victorian idea of a male bird singing from his perch, while his mate tends to their young, has been put in perspective by much recent DNA research. This has established that in a surprisingly large number of cases (up to 50% in some species), the young that both parents invest so much energy in to bringing up were actually fathered by a male from another pair.

Further analysis has shown that in many songbird species, females actively seek copulations with other males, often ones with richer song repertoires (better chat-up lines), while maintaining the pair bond with their current mate. The picture is rather more complex and intriguing than it seemed. So once mated, a male sings to aggravate other males and deter them from fertilising his mate. Meanwhile she is deciding whether he or another male will fertilise her, so the male also has to impress her enough with his song to retain her loyalty. But he is also an opportunist; given half a chance, he will fertilise any other female that his song also succeeds in attracting.

Staicer, Spector & Horn (1996) sum up the circumstances in which they see most songbirds extremely well: "The social relationships between territorial birds can be visualised as a complex and dynamic web, manifested in territory ownership, pair-bonds, and genetic offspring. Territory edges and contents (e.g., mates, nest sites, and young) may change from day to day… When a neighbour disappears or a new bird arrives, the remaining birds shift their territory boundaries; a mate's presence, reproductive state, and behavior may also change daily and clearly influence the behavior of a territorial bird… For example, when a female selects a nest site peripheral to her mate's territory, he typically enlarges the territory to encompass the area surrounding the nest." They point out that nest predation is very high in some species and as a consequence, abandonment of the territory is quite likely. When a territory becomes vacant, the neighbours will try to take it over within a few days or even hours. Unmated first-year males will also float around a group of territories waiting for this, or hoping for the death of a male so they can take its place or insert a new territory in that range. Unpaired males will also take up residence on the edge of a series of territories, often in less than optimal habitat, and sing throughout the summer.

Part 7: Magnus Robb and 'The Blackcaps'

Mimicry, hybridisation, mixed singers and dialect

Magnus is a composer by vocation, and his compositions have titles a birder can be proud of, like *Ancient language of the birds, and Sprosser*. For one of his compositions, *Summoning Dawn; the rubythroat dreaming*, he recorded a Siberian Rubythroat *L calliope*, slowed down its phrases and scored them for voice. The BBC who commissioned the piece then arranged a performance on the radio.

Songbirds are also inspired this way and mimicry provides most of a bird's raw material for its own fine compositions. Young songbirds experiment and copy their parents and on returning to their breeding areas then copy the song phrases of the other birds nearby, often the children of their father's old neighbours. The adults on the other hand behave more like avian DJ's than composers. They take traditional sound samples of other species, and mix and match them with whatever is fashionable in their neighbourhood at the time. Immigrants bring in new song phrases that catch on. They do it all to impress the girls or the neighbours.

Sounds like your local music scene? We can take the analogy further. Listen to this band; we'll call them 'The Blackcaps'. One of their fathers took a Great Tit phrase, sampled it, and incorporated it into the local song repertoire. Like a number-one

record, it's become very popular, and now they're all singing it **(CD2-34)**. I don't know how long they've been singing along this way but research suggests that new song types develop in chaffinches in less than 300 years (Sick 1939, Armstrong 1963) while Indigo Buntings *Passerina cyanea* can "diverge from a common ancestral song theme in less than ten years" (Baptista in litt).

Blackcap *Sylvia atricapilla* Pollensa, Mallorca, Spain, 06:00, 21 July 2004. Several males near and far, imitating the song of Great Tit. Background: Common Wood Pigeon *Columba palumbus*, fledgling Common Blackbird *Turdus merula*, Sardinian Warbler *S melanocephala* and House Sparrow *Passer domesticus*. 04.017.MC.01230.11 — **CD2-34**

Blackcap *Sylvia atricapilla*, Hook Head, Wexford, Ireland, 30 October 1987 *(Killian Mullarney)*

Marsh Warbler *Acrocephalus palustris*, Byelorussia, May 2003 *(René Pop)*

The success of a particular song phrase in a neighbourhood's shared repertoire depends on who is singing it. If a first-year male arrives late in the season singing a new phrase, it is not likely to catch on: he is not likely to be very popular with the females. Females are impressed with males already established in the neighbourhood with a rich repertoire and reward them with extra-pair copulation. A new song by an established and successful male, sung early in the breeding season, has a far greater chance of being copied. The first-year birds in a group of songbirds start with a lot of experimentation and then revert to the songs being sung by the surrounding adults. One adult singing the new 'number one' doesn't guarantee its success either as it needs to be sung by several males to become successful. This way, song repertoires slowly evolve through improvisation and the introduction of new songs by immigrants.

CD2-35   **Common Starling** *Sturnus vulgaris* East Holm, Orkney, Scotland, 09:00, 14 October 2005. Song of an adult perched on a wire, with imitations including Eurasian Curlew *Numenius arquata*, Black-headed Gull *Larus ridibundus*, House Sparrow *Passer domesticus* and even the sound of a flock of starlings taking off. Background: other Common Starlings and House Sparrows. 05.026.MR.14501.01

In the context of identifying birds by sound, mimicry should not be seen as a big problem. Most mimics quickly betray their real identity through the use of other diagnostic sounds in their song, which are unique to their own species, or through the framework the imitations are made to fit into. Listen to the structure of this Common Starling song (**CD2-35**). Starlings are well known for being mimics, but what is less well known is that they incorporate these imitations at a set point in each song. They start with a series of whistles from their collection, they then go into a bit of garbled song including up to 20 imitations

of other bird sounds but also noises like telephones etc. They then finish with a series of rattle phrases followed with a flourish of high pitched notes. Catchpole & Slater (1993) explain all this and go on to point out that starlings seldom finish a song as they are easily distracted in which case they just start it again.

Common Starlings don't just go for any imitations though. A research group that tried to tutor starlings by playing them songs on tape recorders failed, as the starlings ignored the songs that they were supposed to learn. After a while the researchers noticed that while ignoring the bird songs, the starlings had "mimicked the sounds of the tape recorder reels turning, the tape hiss, and the coughing of the human 'in charge'" (West et al 1983).

Common Redstart *Phoenicurus phoenicurus* incorporates imitations into its song, although you have to be really fast to hear them and they are normally at the end of the song phrase. Even relatively simple songs may be adorned with a sound or two pinched from another species and, in many parts of Europe, Common Chaffinches sometimes use what sounds exactly like a Great Spotted Woodpecker's *kit* call in their songs, normally at the end. It is surprising how easy it is to get caught out by this when you are searching for rare woodpeckers in eastern Europe. Listen to calls of Great Spotted (**CD2-36a**). Then see if you can hear the same call at the end of a chaffinch song (**CD2-36b**).

One of the main ways songbirds acquire their repertoires is through song matching. By copying each other and repeating what they just heard, they reinforce the popularity of certain song phrases. The recording of song-duelling Thrush Nightingales in **CD2-37** was made on the 9th of May, shortly after the birds returned to their breeding grounds in north-eastern Poland. Both were probably still unpaired, so they were singing in the hope of attracting a mate, and to mark out their territories. In the recording, you can clearly hear that the two birds share much of their repertoire. The slightly closer bird on the left sings phrases that are answered by very similar ones given by the slightly more distant bird on the right. From 0:54, the roles are reversed and the bird on the right takes the initiative.

CD2-36a
0:00-0:19
Great Spotted Woodpecker *Dendrocopos major* Amsterdamse Waterleidingduinen, Noord-Holland, Netherlands, 10:18, 13 March 2000. *Kit* calls, one of three birds present; another one calls excitedly later in the recording. Background: European Robin *Erithacus rubecula*, Song Thrush *Turdus philomelus*, Short-toed Treecreeper *Certhia brachydactyla* and Common Chaffinch *Fringilla coelebs*. 00.001.MR.10620.01

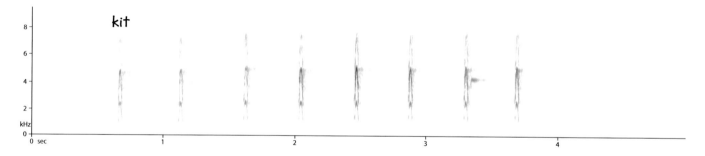

CD2-36b
0:20-0:28
Common Chaffinch *Fringilla coelebs* Biebrza marshes, Podłaskie, Poland, 05:29, 20 April 2003. Song ending with woodpecker *kit*. Background: Common Chaffinch *Fringilla coelebs*. 03.007.AB.01855.02

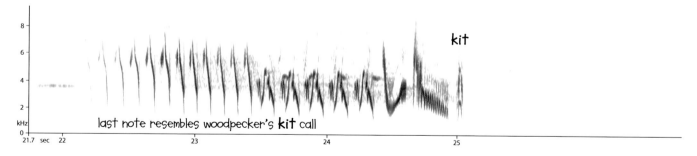

CD2-37
Thrush Nightingale *Luscinia luscinia* Bagno Ławki, Biebrza marshes, Podłaskie, Poland, 23:00, 9 May 2005. A song duel between neighbouring males, left and right of the microphone, very early in the breeding season. The left hand bird is in the leading role at first, then at 0:54 the right hand bird takes over. Background: Great Bittern *Botaurus stellaris*, Tawny Owl *Strix aluco*, a third Thrush Nightingale and Savi's Warbler *Locustella luscinioides*. 05.009.MR.05532.11

Marsh Warbler is the best rapper in natural history and its song is astonishing in its speed and richness. An individual bird will use around 70 samples (imitations), with over 200 species known to be in the repertoire. This was researched in a series of papers by Françoise Dowsett-Lemaire (eg, 1979), who used sonagram technology to illustrate this diversity. She discovered that Marsh Warblers learn their song from other birds that they meet on their travels, both European and African species. **CD2-38** is a recording of a Marsh Warbler on territory in the Netherlands. Finnish birders say that if you are unable to keep up with the impersonations in a song, it's a Marsh Warbler (and not a Blyth's Reed Warbler). Not only are there lots of different imitations, but Marsh Warbler makes it more difficult to keep track of them by constantly speeding up or slowing down. We have made it easier for you to hear a few of them; in **CD2-39**, you can hear several imitations of familiar European species cut from the first 20 seconds of the recording, each followed by the real thing. Later in the Marsh Warbler song, see if you can also hear the following European species: House Martin *Delichon urbicum*, Willow Warbler, Common Linnet and European Greenfinch. More exotic species the Marsh Warbler heard along its migration route include Purple Sunbird *Nectarinia asiatica* of eastern Arabia and southern Asia (imitated at 0:20) and Blue-cheeked Bee-eater *Merops persicus* of the Middle East and much of Africa (imitated briefly at 2:02). Françoise Dowsett-Lemaire would also have recognised many African species in the recording, but that's not our forte.

CD2-38   **Marsh Warbler** *Acrocephalus palustris* Horsterwold, Flevoland, Netherlands, 22 June 2001. Song full of imitations of other bird species. Background: female Tufted Duck *Aythya fuligula*, Winter Wren *Troglodytes troglodytes* and Willow Warbler *Phylloscopus trochilus*. 01.027.MR.15737.10

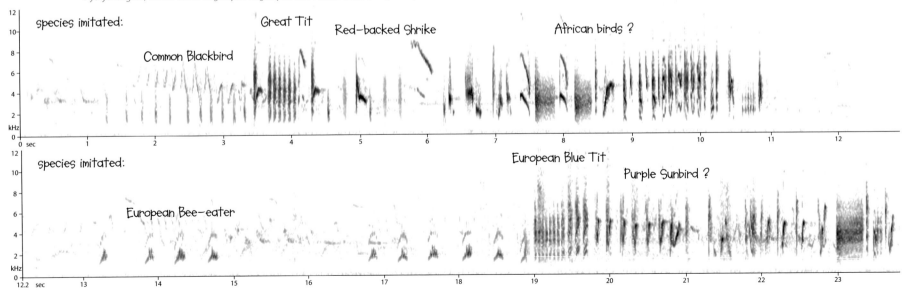

Some species imitated during the first 20 seconds of the preceding track. In each instance, you will hear the Marsh Warbler's *Acrocephalus palustris* rendition first, followed by the real thing.

0:00 – 0:02 **Marsh Warbler** imitating Common Blackbird *Turdus merula* (CD2-38: 0:01 – 0:03)
0:03 – 0:05 **Common Blackbird** Madeira, 3 April 2002. 02.013.MR.12314.01

0:07 – 0:08 **Marsh Warbler** imitating Great Tit *Parus major* (CD2-38: 0:03 – 0:04)
0:09   0:10 **Great Tit** Netherlands, 19 October 2001. 01.017.AB.12027.31

0:12 – 0:13 **Marsh Warbler** imitating Red-backed Shrike *Lanius collurio* (CD2-38: 0:05 – 0:06)
0:14 – 0:15 **Red-backed Shrike** Sweden, 21 July 2001. 01.016.AB.10357.01

0:17 – 0:22 **Marsh Warbler** imitating European Bee-eater *Merops apiaster* (CD2-38: 0:13 – 0:19)
0:23 – 0:28 **European Bee-eater** Greece, 30 April 2002. 02.020.MR.15529.01

0:30 – 0:31 **Marsh Warbler** imitating European Blue Tit *Cyanistes caeruleus* (CD2-38: 0:19 – 0:20)
0:32 – 0:34 **European Blue Tit** Netherlands 2 May 2000. 00.004.AB.13959.01

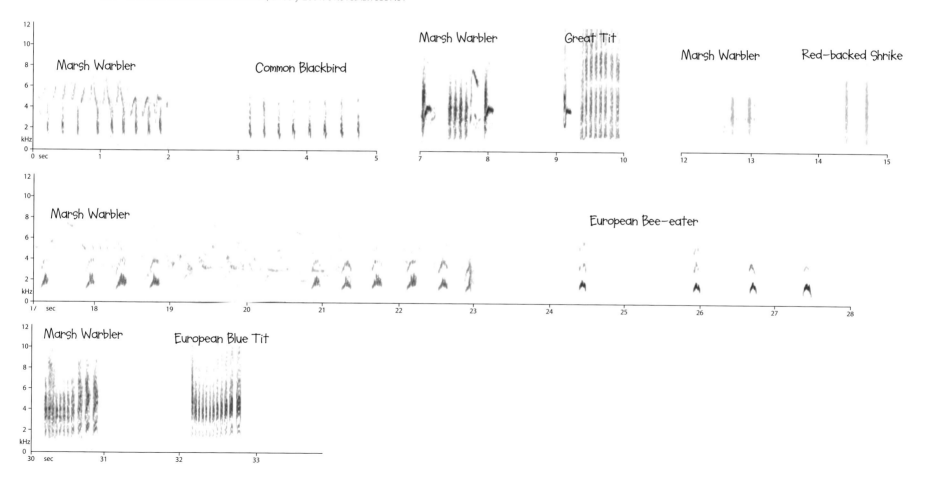

While Marsh Warblers are well known for imitating, Blyth's Reed Warbler and European Reed Warbler also like to have a go. These two, however, sing at a much more steady pace. European Reed's song is medium paced with a very regular, even boring, delivery. Listening for the song tempo can be particularly important in recognizing a European Reed that indulges in more obvious mimicry than usual. Have a listen to this song of a mature bird on its territory (**CD2-40**), with only a few noticeable imitations (these include Marsh Harrier *Circus aeruginosus*, Eurasian Coot and Common Tern).

Next, listen to the typically slow and repetitive song of a mature Blyth's Reed Warbler established on its territory (**CD2-41**). Imitations heard during the first 30 seconds include yellow wagtail *Motacilla,* Common Rosefinch, Yellowhammer *E citrinella*, Mealy Redpoll and Tree Sparrow *P montanus*. If you are able to keep up with the imitations, it's more likely to be a Blyth's Reed than a Marsh Warbler.

CD2-40   **European Reed Warbler** *Acrocephalus scirpaceus* Oostvaardersplassen, Flevoland, Netherlands, 05:00, 15 May 2000. Song with only a few imitations. Background: Winter Wren *Troglodytes troglodytes*, Common Blackbird *Turdus merula*, Sedge Warbler *Acrocephalus schoenobaenus*, Garden Warbler *Sylvia borin* and Penduline Tit *Remiz pendulinus*. 00.008.AB.13103.02

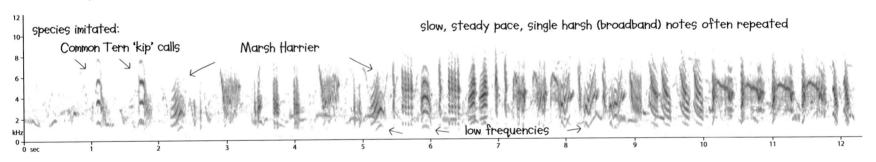

CD2-41   **Blyth's Reed Warbler** *Acrocephalus dumetorum* Musko, Tohmajarvi, Pohjois-Karjala, Finland, 10 July 2003. Song with imitations. Background: Willow Warbler *Phylloscopus trochilus*. 03.004.DF.04847.11

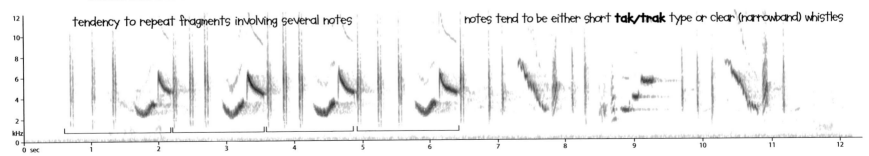

Marsh Warbler and its familiars are well known mimics. What is not understood is that **all** passerines include mimicry somewhere in their repertoires, and when identifying them by their sounds it helps to be aware of this. While making these recordings, each of us have been caught out by Eurasian Jay's habit of flying around copying everything from a firework to a Common Buzzard *B buteo*, a Northern Goshawk *A gentilis* or a Tawny Owl *S aluco*.

There are various theories as to why birds imitate. In the case of Eurasian Jay it is thought to be an aspect of mobbing. In others it's been shown that the bird with the largest repertoire gets a mate first. Kroodsma (1982) suggested that when young birds were in a late brood or at the edge of the species' breeding range, they didn't hear enough song of their own species, at the time when they are most receptive to learning it. A very strange song, recorded in the town of Stromness in Orkney, Scotland, seems to be a very peculiar example of this **(CD2-42)**. Magnus was hoping it might have been a trans-Atlantic vagrant, so he was disappointed when a male Common Chaffinch popped into view. It seems that this bird's song had taken some inspiration from a Barn Swallow *Hirundo rustica* (first three phrases) and a Winter Wren (final phrase). In Orkney, the density of Common Chaffinches is extremely low. Perhaps this bird's father had disappeared when it was at the critical age for song learning. If it hatched in Orkney, there may have been no other chaffinches nearby for it to learn from.

CD2-42   **Common Chaffinch** *Fringilla coelebs* Stromness, Orkney, Scotland, 7 July 2001. Aberrant songs resembling Barn Swallow *Hirundo rustica* and Winter Wren *Troglodytes troglodytes*. 01.031.MR.00625.31

Mixed singers and hybridisation

When rare vagrants turn up, sounds can be very useful in getting the correct identification. It's not so useful if the bird is suspected of being a hybrid. The problem in this instance is called mixed singing, and it occurs when a bird of one species partly or completely learns the songs of a close relative. For instance, this may occur when a less abundant species adopts song characters of a more abundant species it is competing with. Mixed singing is common where Icterine Warbler and Melodious Warbler *H polyglotta* meet. When there is local competition between the two species it is normally Melodious that copies the features of Icterine songs (Secondi et al 2003). In a German study in Schleswig-Holstein, Germany, where Thrush Nightingale and Common Nightingale overlap, the researchers came to the conclusion that Thrush Nightingale was the more easily influenced when they discovered that only one out of 200 Common Nightingales, but 67 out of 239 Thrush Nightingales were mixed singers (Lille 1988). Research into Pied Flycatcher *F hypoleuca* and Collared Flycatcher in two different contact zones also found a lot of mixed singing, and it has been suggested that mixed singing tends to occur more often in new contact zones (Haavie et al 2004).

Researchers and captive breeders have devoted a lot of time to studying the songs and calls that result when two species hybridise. However, many of the things that are observed in captivity don't seem to occur in the wild. One of the best studied examples of hybridisation in the wild is between two American warblers, Blue-winged Warbler *Vermivora pinus* and Golden-winged Warbler *V chrysoptera*. The most common hybrid variation is called Brewster's Warbler and the rarer one is

Lawrence's Warbler. The very simple songs of these hybrids can be like either parent, and occasionally they sing complete songs of both parent species in alternation. Interestingly, researchers have found that they never sing mixed songs (Confer 1992). A more complicated situation is found where the breeding ranges of Common Chiffchaff and Iberian Chiffchaff meet in the western Pyrenees. Mixed songs are frequently encountered, and in this case researchers have found that the majority of mixed singers are hybrids, as are quite a few of the birds with pure Common or Iberian song (Bensch et al 2002).

As we've seen there can be many reasons for unrecognisable songs and when faced with an apparent mixed singer, bear the following points in mind. Mixed singers are not necessarily hybrids, and conversely, hybrids will not necessarily sing mixed songs. There are no hard and fast rules, and apparent mixed singing can sometimes be an indication of immaturity; the bird may eventually settle for the correct song. Equally, territorial disputes can elicit ultra-crystallised song and this should also be eliminated from the running. In species pairs where mixed singing occurs, there is normally a dominant species, as in examples of Common Nightingale, Icterine Warbler and Common Chiffchaff. Mixed songs usually occur in the less dominant species, and calls may be a good indication of which species a mixed singer belongs to, unless it's a hybrid.

Dialect

Dialect is the general term used for any and for all of the above. It describes in a broad way the fashions that prevail as the different schools settle down for the breeding season. It's the Jets and Sharks in West Side Story, gangs that have their own slang words and turf. That is all dialect is and it's not just songbirds that play these games. Listen to these two groups of Common Quails *Coturnix coturnix* when they return to the breeding grounds in Kazakhstan **(CD2-43)** and Gran Canaria, Canary Islands **(CD2-44)**. At first they sound like any other Common Quail, singing about wet lips, each individual in its own little circle of around a dozen birds. An individual can identify each of its neighbours by the first *whet* note. Now compare the rhythm of the song, for this is how the group identifies itself (Guyomarc'h et al 1984). This creates a dialect specific to the group.

Common Quail *Coturnix coturnix* Between Korgalzhyn and Astana, Aqmola Oblast, Kazakhstan, 29 May 2003. A different assembly of singing quails; the *kiss-me-quick* song is delivered rather more slowly and a harsh note can be heard between the *me* and the *quick* notes. Background: Eurasian Skylark *Alauda arvensis*, Booted Warbler *Acrocephalus caligatus* and Red-headed Bunting *Emberiza bruniceps*. 03.022.AB.04850.01 **CD2-43**

Common Quail *Coturnix coturnix* Gran Canaria, Canary Islands, Spain, 19 April 2001. In this assembly of singing quails, all deliver their *kiss-me-quick* song rather rapidly. Background: Corn Buntings *Emberiza calandra*. 01.013.MR.02110.01 **CD2-44**

It all comes down to mimicry in the end. Kids copying adults, adults copying their neighbours and all of them copying other species. This goes on and on till almost by accident they can no longer speak with someone they used to understand. Rather like a story Peter Ustinov would tell of a conductor who had difficulty instructing his orchestra, as he had forgotten his own language without taking the precaution of learning a new one. In birds, when all communication breaks down between sets of individuals that's when a new species is born.

Part 8: Twitching and taxonomy

How sounds define species and their importance in conservation

I've known and liked James Lidster since he was a fledgling. It has to be said that before he became Dorset Bird Recorder, Sunbird tour leader and British Birds Rarity Committee member, he was a twitcher. Surgically attached to his pager when younger, he was so concerned about being thought a twitcher he wouldn't put a bird club sticker in the rear window of his car. When cornered, he admitted that it was in case some girl might notice and consider him too nerdy. I don't really like being called a twitcher either although the competitive aspect of listing birds has motivated me. I am very keen on my garden list, and my Poole Harbour list, and my Dorset list and winning bird races with big day lists. I didn't list all my lists there in case you got the idea that I'm a bit nerdy. Listing is the starting point for many of us. This interest then takes us to taxonomy.

Taxonomy is the science of classifying. As birders, taxa – species, families and so on – are first and foremost tools of thought. We all use them to break down the natural diversity into manageable, named chunks our brains can cope with. All of us are taxonomists at heart, or at least we were. Starting at less than one year old, we sorted animals into 'four-legged ones with tail that go *woof*', or 'those with wings and a beak that go *cheep*'. Like birds learning to sing, we built on our repertoire as we grew up,

until we had a fully crystallised set of bird names not much longer than 'seagull', 'sparrow', 'duck', 'eagle', and 'owl'. Those of us who took it a stage further were already evolving into birders, but even birders are not immune to crystallisation: our taxonomy was already becoming more passive. More and more, we were happy to learn and adopt the names in our field guides, rather than try to make sense of the variety for ourselves.

Ian Lewis at Poole, Dorset, 20 April 2006 *(Arnoud B van den Berg)*

That's not the case with everyone. As previous chairman of the Dorset bird club, bird pub stalwart Ian Lewis is a twitcher on a grand scale because he is foremost a world life lister. He wants to see as many different species in the world as possible and has

'Laughing Moorhen' *Gallinula chloropus cachinnans*, Wakodahatchee, Palm Beach, Florida, USA, 9 February 2005 *(Arnoud B van den Berg)*. One of the birds on CD2-51.

seen about 6700 so far. He worked out very early that to achieve his aim would take a lifetime so he had to visit birds in countries where birds are in peril first while he was still in robust health. This means that many of his stories concern snakes, toilets or a combination of both. His grasp of geography and a bird's status in each country is comprehensive and the memory of being a competitor in the bi-annual quizzes he organises still wakes me in a sweat, as I dream of being played my own bird sound recordings and not recognising them. At the pub, what you can and cannot tick has created some interesting arguments. With "can I tick a bird I've only heard?" being a regular. For me the question is "can you tick a winter plumage dowitcher you haven't heard?" Obviously, yes, of course you can tick a bird you have only heard. What matters is not the sense with which you've identified the bird, but the accuracy of the identification itself. Ian keeps a separate list of heard onlys so my arguments have only partially won him over. What involves both our interests though is what song characteristics create a new species.

Becker (1982) tried to define what kinds of song characters birds themselves use in species identification. He was able to conclude that some types of variation play little or no role in this, while others do time and again. Song length, for example, is rarely a species trademark, because this varies so much between and within individuals, as we saw with the Blackcaps. Variations in the intensity of the song and subtleties of harmonics are both poor means of encoding species identity. As we have heard, distance and prevalent acoustics can change these aspects quite drastically by the time the song reaches its intended audience. Things that do work include differences in the syntax or structuring of a song, the proportions and degree of constrast between parts. Or it can be rhythmic patterns, such as pulse rates and differences in the length of gaps between similar notes. Frequency range can also be a key difference between close relatives and, finally, patterns of frequency change within individual notes, which we can see as different shapes on a sonagram, may be a key feature. Another species that is hard to tick without hearing is Iberian Chiffchaff. Four of Becker's key differences can be found between advertising songs of Common Chiffchaff (CD2-45) and Iberian Chiffchaff (CD2-46). As you can see in the sonagram, these diagnostic differences include the syntax or structure, length of gaps between notes, the upper limit of frequency range and finally the shape of individual notes (Salomon & Hemim 1992).

CD2-45 Common Chiffchaff *Phylloscopus collybita* Kennemerduinen, Bloemendaal, Noord-Holland, Netherlands, 28 March 2002. Advertising song in a recently reoccupied territory. Background: Common Chaffinch *Fringilla coelebs* and Eurasian Siskin *Carduelis spinus*. 02.011.MR.12344.01

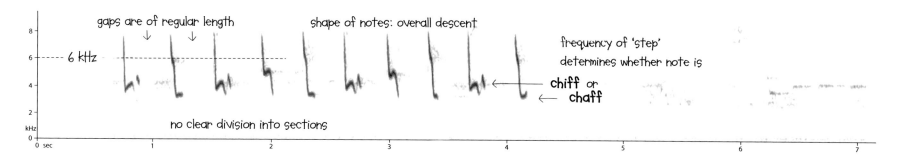

gaps are of regular length

shape of notes: overall descent

6 kHz

frequency of 'step' determines whether note is

chiff or
chaff

no clear division into sections

CD2-46 Iberian Chiffchaff *Phylloscopus ibericus* Erro, Navarra, Spain, 06:50, 26 June 2002. Advertising song with diagnostic three-part structure. Background: Winter Wren *Troglodytes troglodytes*, songs and calls of other Iberian Chiffchaffs, Blackcap *Sylvia atricapilla*. 02.025.AB.15652.11

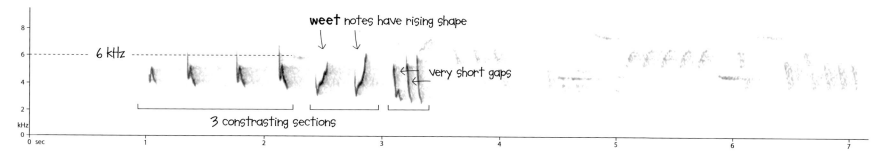

weet notes have rising shape

6 kHz

very short gaps

3 constrasting sections

Conservation

I suggested at the beginning of this section that a bird's status, species or not, is all to do with a human need to classify things, but there is a frighteningly important side to it all: conservation. Whether a bird is one species or another can influence everything from the building of an airport to the fate of a forest. Since vocalisations can form a diagnostic feature for a species, one may argue that undervaluing bioacoustics can dramatically effect biodiversity. It seems as if we are all waiting for a visionary taxonomist with a holistic view who can pull together all aspects of a bird's biology, and hammer in place a concept that will guide conservationists and birders through the storms and tempests of climate change.

Consider the fate of these European Storm-petrels *Hydrobates pelagicus* that breed in a sea cave on a small island, bathed in the night lights of the busy Spanish resort of Benidorm **(CD2-47)**. The petrels belong to the Mediterranean subspecies *H p melitensis*, a warm water population thought to breed in fairly low numbers throughout the Mediterranean, differing diagnostically from North Atlantic nominate birds in measurements. The island is visited by many tourists daily, and is also home to a colony of Yellow-legged Gulls. Consequently, the petrels are vulnerable not only to climate change but to disturbance and predation, and this is a story which is repeated at other colonies, many of which are close to popular tourist areas and the gulls they attract.

There are differences between the calls of *melitensis* and its North Atlantic nominate *pelagicus* counterpart, which breeds most numerously in Britain and Ireland **(CD2-48)**, and perhaps these two taxa are better treated as separate species. To make these recordings, Magnus had already visited several North Atlantic *pelagicus* colonies and was familiar with their sounds before seabird expert Eduardo Mínguez took him to the Islote de Benidorm islet. There, one particular call of *melitensis* immediately struck him as different. Eduardo mimics this agonistic call, and the petrels respond well to his imitations. The call is the same in both sexes (James 1984), and it is probably equivalent to the 'flight calls' of Madeiran Storm-petrel (cf CD2-24), but in the two, smaller, more vulnerable European Storm-petrels they are never given in flight. Whether the calls recorded on Islote de Benidorm are representative for the whole of the Mediterranean remains to be seen but, judging from recordings (Moreno 2000), the European Storm-petrels breeding off Lanzarote, Canary Islands, may also belong to *melitensis*.

European (Mediterranean) Storm-petrel *Hydrobates pelagicus melitensis* Islote de Benidorm, País Valenciano, Spain, 7 August 2002. 'Agonistic calls': *Doerrr-Chik*. The purring calls ending with a wheezing sound are 'burrow' calls, only given by males. Some of the agonistic calls may be from the same male. The constant high-pitched peeping sound in the background is made by nestlings. 02.038.MR.03333b.00 **CD2-47**

European (North Atlantic) Storm-petrel *Hydrobates pelagicus pelagicus* Mousa, Shetland, Scotland, 00:00, 12 July 2001. 'Agonistic calls': *m-Terrrr-Chik*. This bird was also heard giving 'burrow' calls, which are only given by males. Background: other European Storm-petrels and Common Snipe *Gallinago gallinago*. 01.032.MR.13443.00 **CD2-48**

Pelagic islands are good places to search for endemics, and the way birds learn their sounds is part of the reason why. Song learning is a major contributing factor in the genesis of new species. The peculiar songs of Madeiran Kinglet *R madeirensis* **(CD2-49)** are thought to have evolved away from an ancestor it has in common with Firecrest **(CD2-50)**. It has often been suggested that island endemics are relicts of birds remaining stationary in appearance and sound while their relatives on the continents evolved into 'other' species, under pressure of more competition or divides caused by ice ages, for instance. It is no coincidence that song learners make up about half of all bird species. The ability to learn songs vastly increases the possibilities for variation, and is thought to have led to an accelleration in the rate at which new species are evolving.

It also introduces additional complications when it comes to looking for diagnostic differences because taxonomists need to be sure that they are comparing birds at a similar stage in the learning process, preferably adult birds with fully crystallised songs.

CD2-49   **Madeiran Kinglet** *Regulus madeirensis* Casa de Queimadas, Madeira, Portugal, morning, 3 April 2002. Fully crystallised song. Background: Madeiran Chaffinch *Fringilla coelebs maderensis*. 02.013.MR.11346.00

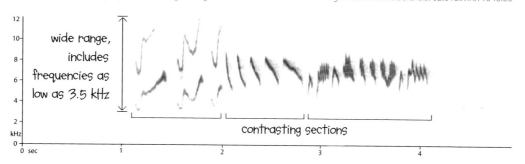

CD2-50   **Firecrest** *Regulus ignicapilla* Parnassos, Greece, 11 May 2002. Fully crystallised song at dawn. Background: Black Redstart *Phoenicurus ochruros*, Mistle Thrush *Turdus viscivorus* and Common Chaffinch *Fringilla coelebs*. 02.024.MR.10741.00

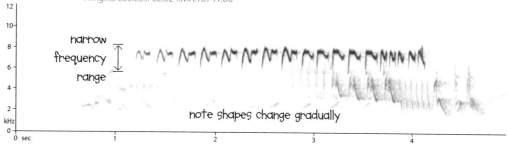

Kroodsma, Vielliard & Stiles (1996) have pointed out that "Many recent studies have revealed that speciation may not be accompanied by much differentiation in plumage... often, the first clue to the true status of these species was provided by a difference in vocalisations, which in turn prompted the discovery of morphological, behavioral, or biochemical differences...".

Recently, much has been written about the use of DNA in working out what is and is not a species, and there has been a move away from using plumage and biometrics as the main indicators. Very often though, it is sounds that give the first hint that a part of a population of birds we always classified under one label has actually evolved into something else. The relative ease with which sound recordings can be obtained, makes sounds the best early warning signals about undervalued or undiscovered biodiversity: birds whose classification needs to be re-evaluated.

Birders can play a part in 'uncovering new biodiversity', not least because their increased mobility is now taking them abroad more often. The observation that 'this species sounds totally different back home' might just be the first of many steps towards realising that it is *not* the same species, even if its plumage appears totally indistinguishable. The separation of Nearctic from Palearctic taxa has also been and probably will continue to be the most productive areas of opportunity for budding taxonomists. So, it is hardly surprising that another side effect of allowing Old World participants to take part in the *World Series of Birding* in New Jersey, was the realisation that in the spring the North American Common Moorhen *Gallinula chloropus cachinnans* sounded nothing like its European counterpart *G c chloropus*. In New Jersey, Common Moorhens are migratory opportunists, waiting for beavers to create new ponds which they quickly populate. An uncommon species, its habitat preference seems to encourage a need to attract a mate or defend territory in a different way. In crepuscular, nocturnal and marsh dwelling birds like petrels, owls and rails, including moorhen, sound is of more importance for pair formation than appearance. Consequently, differences in sounds can indicate that speciation has taken place sooner than any other feature.

Whoever named the North American subspecies of moorhen *cachinnans* must have suspected that it was something quite different. As explained with the gulls (Caspian Gull), *cachinnans* means 'laughing', and this American has a laugh, louder and somehow more brash, never heard from moorhens in the Western Palearctic. Listen to these birds recorded in Florida **(CD2-51)** and compare them with Common Moorhens recorded in Morocco **(CD2-52)**. The 'Laughing Moorhen' sounds far more rail-like. Its appearance is different too, especially the shape and size of its frontal shield, and it also has a longer bill and a more reddish brown back and rump. But these visible differences pale into insignificance when compared to the huge difference in sound.

CD2-51 **'Laughing Moorhen'** *Gallinula chloropus cachinnans* Palm Beach, Florida, USA, 08:26, 9 February 2005. Infectious brash laughter of North American moorhens. Outbursts of several birds in close succession. At 0:06-0:09 there is a different chattering call consisting of paired notes. Background: Limpkin *Aramus guarauna*, Eurasian Collared Dove *Streptopelia decaocto* and Boat-tailed Grackle *Quiscalus major*. 05.002.AB.10019.01

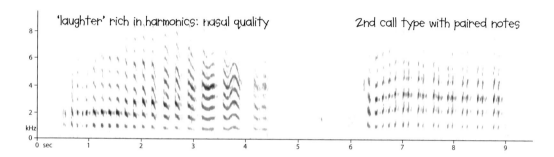

'Laughing Moorhen' *Gallinula chloropus cachinnans*, Wakoda-hatchee, Palm Beach, Florida, USA, 9 February 2005 *(Arnoud B van den Berg)*. One of the birds on CD2-51.

CD2-52 **Common Moorhen** *Gallinula chloropus chloropus* Oued Massa, Chtouka-Ait Baha, Morocco, 07:00, 5 November 2005. Various calls of Western Palearctic moorhens. This bird has a similar chattering series of paired notes like the one in the recording of 'Laughing Moorhen', but what we would consider the 'normal' call replaces the long series of 'laughing'. Background: Grey Heron *Ardea cinerea*, Eurasian Coot *Fulica atra*, Common Kingfisher *Alcedo atthis*, Common Bulbul *Pycnonotus barbatus* and Cetti's Warbler *Cettia cetti*. 05.018.AB.12351.01

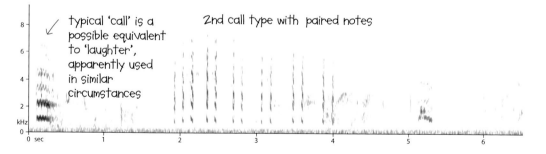

Common Moorhen *Gallinula chloropus chloropus*, Merwedekanaal, Utrecht, Netherlands, 17 February 1991 *(Arnoud B van den Berg)*. Look for differences in frontal shield, head shape, structure and colour of upperparts from 'Laughing Moorhen' of America.

139

Sometimes things are less easy to determine. In recent years, a number of 'Maghreb' chaffinches, either Atlas *F c africana* or Tunisian *F c spodiogenys*, have been found in western Europe with European Common Chaffinches returning from North Africa in the spring. Both 'Maghreb' chaffinch males differ from European chaffinches in, for instance, having a green mantle, ear coverts the same bluish colour as the crown, and paler pinkish underparts (van den Berg & The Sound Approach 2005). In **CD2-53 and 54** you can hear examples of their songs. While both sound a little exotic compared to Common Chaffinch, we shouldn't be comparing these two recordings, because the song in the Atlas recording is plastic and we will need more recordings to work out whether *africana's* songs are different enough from European's to suggest species status. However the *chep* calls you can hear in both recordings (right from the start) are quite unlike anything familiar to Arnoud and Magnus from European chaffinches. They also believe these sounds are diagnostic for separating them from European birds.

Atlas Chaffinch *Fringilla coelebs africana*, male, Larache, Morocco, 27 March 2006 *(Arnoud B van den Berg)*

CD2-53   **Atlas Chaffinch** *Fringilla coelebs africana* Forêt de Cèdres, Moyen Atlas, Morocco, 06:24, 25 March 2002. Song of a male, with other individuals calling and singing in the background. Background: European Robin *Erithacus rubecula*. 02.003.AB.00040.10

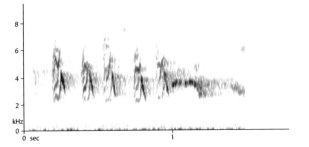

Atlas Chaffinch *Fringilla coelebs africana*, male, Larache, Morocco, 27 March 2006 *(Arnoud B van den Berg)*

CD2-54a   **Tunisian Chaffinch** *Fringilla coelebs spodiogenys*, male, Cap Bon, Nabeul, Haouaria, Tunisia, 06:57, 2 May 2005. Song and calls of a male. Background: migrating European Bee-eater *Merops apiaster*, Winter Wren *Troglodytes troglodytes*, Sardinian Warbler *Sylvia melanocephala*, Spanish Sparrow *Passer hispaniolensis*, European Serin *Serinus serinus* and Corn Bunting *Emberiza calandra*. 05.006.AB.12118.01

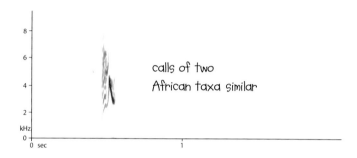

Tunisian Chaffinch *Fringilla coelebs spodiogenys*, male, Arram, Gabès, Tunisia, 1 May 2005 *(René Pop)*

See CD1-80a: **Common Chaffinch** *Fringilla coelebs*

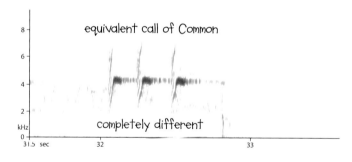

the same *chep* call. Molecular data suggest however that *africana* and *spodiogenys* are less related to each other than *africana* is to European. So, if it were only according to DNA studies, Atlas Chaffinch would be split from European and then Tunisian would have to be split from Atlas, despite the similarity of their sounds.

During the course of the past 15 years we have looked at a number of taxa in the same way, wondering if they differed enough vocally to be considered species, Yellow wagtails, for instance, or the two subspecies of Black-tailed Godwits. Thankfully neither these nor the Atlas or Tunisian Chaffinch appear to be greatly threatened at the present time.

In this case sounds don't make a case for Atlas and Tunisian Chaffinch to be separated from each other, despite minor differences in plumage mentioned in our paper, as they share

Redefining relationships by sound

Do you sometimes think that we make things to complicated? In 1827 von Baldenstein came up with the idea of describing Melodious Warbler as a *Hippolais*. Then others took three birds from the *Sylvia* and two other genera and put them in von Baldenstein's genus. History suggests it was wrong but this is the problem if you use only skins and skeletons to reach these conclusions. It lasted over 180 years until DNA studies challenged it. Had sound been the defining criteria the *Hippolais* would have been part of the *Acrocephalus* warblers and would never have been considered a separate genus. And unlike DNA, unheard of only a few decades ago, songs and calls have always been available for study. All the *Hippolais* songs and calls fit very comfortably within *Acrocephalus*. Now as the various taxonomic bodies disassemble *Hippolais* some are creating a new genus '*Iduna*'. Lets look at it from The Sound Approach point of view before another 180 years pass.

Two of the *Hippolais* that have created a lot of interest are Booted Warbler *A caligatus* and Sykes's Warbler *A rama* (lets follow our beliefs and the CSNA and call them '*Acrocephalus*'). These two species' songs, while fitting into *Acrocephalus* very comfortably, also differ from each other in striking ways. Adult Sykes's (**CD2-55**) follows most *Acrocephalus* in singing a stream of song which contains the odd impersonation. The song jumps abruptly and rapidly between high and low sections, and doesn't accelerate or rise in pitch. With its steady unchanging and fast tempo it can sound like the ultimate *Acrocephalus*, European Reed Warbler, but turbocharged. Booted's adult song rarely repeats adjacent notes. As in all *Acrocephalus* it alternates between low and high notes but it has a unique spiralling quality (**CD2-56**). Starting quiet and low, it rises, gains volume and accelerates a little, twisting and turning. The most obvious difference between the two is that Sykes's regularly repeats notes, often three times or more repetitively, which eliminates any spiralling effects.

These recordings were made when Magnus visited Kazakhstan in 2000, where he joined Kazakh ornithologist Andrei Gavrilov and a group of other interested birders on a visit to a site where Booted Warbler and Sykes's Warbler had been discovered breeding side by side. This confirmed what had already been suspected for a long time: that these are best treated as two separate species (Sangster et al 1998).

Booted Warbler *Acrocephalus caligatus*, Korgalzhyn lake, Aqmola Oblast, Kazakhstan, 18 May 2003 *(Arnoud B van den Berg)*. Same bird as on CD2-56.

CD2-55   **Sykes's Warbler** *Acrocephalus rama* Kyzyl-Kol, Yuzhnyy Kazakhstan, Kazakhstan, 14 May 2000. Typical song of a bird recently returned to its tamarisk habitat. Background: Grey-headed Wagtail *Motacilla thunbergi* and Greenish Warbler *Phylloscopus trochiloides*. 00.031.MR.05103.00

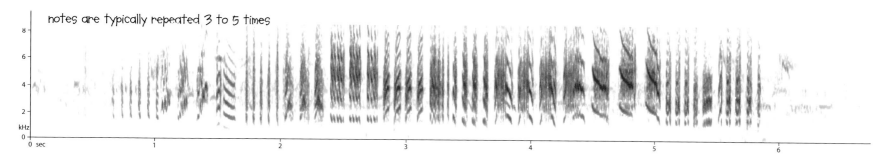

notes are typically repeated 3 to 5 times

CD2-56   **Booted Warbler** *Acrocephalus caligatus* Korgalzhyn lake, Aqmola Oblast, Kazakhstan, 16:45, 18 May 2003. Song in a tiny garden in a settlement in the steppes. Background: Sykes's Blue-headed Wagtail *Motacilla flava beema* and Paddyfield Warbler *A agricola*. 03.016.AB.14639.01

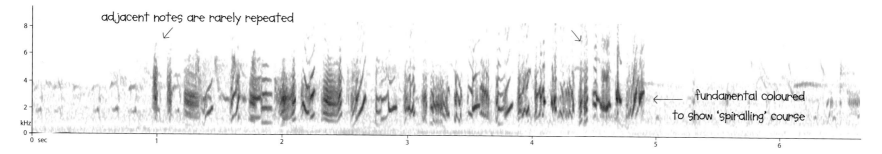

adjacent notes are rarely repeated

fundamental coloured to show 'spiralling' course

143

Booted and Sykes's Warbler's calls

Acrocephalus warblers in the WP use both *tak* or *chak* type sounds and rattling, chattering or churring type calls in their repertoire. As a recent paper in Birding World has shown (Lindholm & Aalto 2005), Booted and Sykes's Warblers have short *zak*-type calls differing from each other, and this is the sound most likely to be heard from an autumn vagrant in western Europe. The calls of Booted are of a longer duration, and sound like somebody striking a match **(CD2-57)**. Sykes's show shorter calls, while sounding more like a tongue-click **(CD2-58)**. Both would fit snugly beside any *Acrocephalus*.

CD2-57   **Booted Warbler** *Acrocephalus caligatus* Between Kytyglysor lake and Nura river, Aqmola Oblast, Kazakhstan, 26 May 2003. Calls of an adult, a presumed male that had been singing as well as feeding a juvenile. Background: Eurasian Skylark *Alauda arvensis* and Tawny Pipit *Anthus campestris*. 03.021.MR.01401d.01

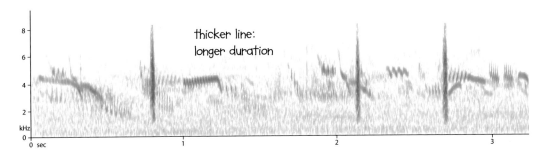

CD2-58   **Sykes's Warbler** *Acrocephalus rama* Kyzyl-Kol, Yuzhnyy Kazakhstan, Kazakhstan, 14 May 2000. Calls of a presumed male that had just been singing. Background: Red-headed Bunting *Emberiza bruniceps*. 00.029.MR.03513a.01

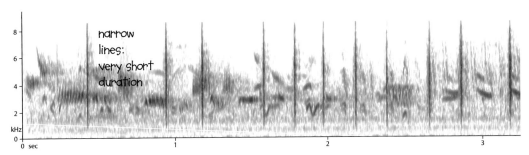

In fact all *Hippolais* possess both *tak* or *chak*, or a slight variation *thak* in Icterine, and rattling, chattering or churring type calls. Icterine also has a somewhat melodic call sounding vaguely reminiscent of the word *hip-po-lais* (rising with the last syllable), which is often incorporated into the song.

In a recent paper Svensson (2001) compares Western Olivaceous Warbler *A opacus* (**CD2-59**) to European Reed Warbler (CD1-09 and **CD2-40**) or Moustached Warbler *A melanopogon*. We agree and as a general rule an adult *Acrocephalus* warbler's tone when singing is unmusical, harsh or buzzy. You couldn't relax to their songs; they aren't uplifting, more irritating if anything. When I first listened to an Eastern Oliveaceous Warbler *A pallidus* singing, I vividly remember being very disappointed when I heard it's acro-like song, not at all sexy. Listen to an Eastern Olivaceous (continuing our theme we call it an *Acrocephalus*) of the Saharan subspecies *A p reiseri*, which Arnoud recorded in Tunisia. Typically for Eastern Olivaceous, it has a habit of repeating sections of song several seconds long before moving on, like a vinyl record with a scratch in it (**CD2-60**). This is a habit it shares with some other *Hippolais*, eg, Upcher's Warbler *H languida* (**CD2-61**), but also with several *Acrocephalus* warblers, especially Blyth's Reed Warbler (cf CD2-41). In fact, it seems difficult to find vocal traits *not* shared between *Hippolais* and *Acrocephalus* warblers, which makes it all the more surprising that sounds were not given more serious consideration in a recent review of the taxonomy of this group (Parkin et al 2004).

Western Olivaceous Warbler *Acrocephalus opacus*, Merzouga, Tafilalt, Morocco, 3 April 2006 *(Arnoud B van den Berg)*. Compare bill length and shape with Eastern (Saharan) Olivaceous Warbler *A pallidus reiseri*, with which it was considered conspecific until recently, despite having a different song.

Eastern (Saharan) Olivaceous Warbler *Acrocephalus pallidus reiseri*, Mareth, Gabès, Tunisia, 1 May 2005 *(René Pop)*. Same bird as on CD2-60.

CD2-59 **Western Olivaceous Warbler** *Acrocephalus opacus* Taliouline, Taroudannt, Morocco, 07:02, 31 March 2002. Song, with resemblance to European Reed Warbler or Moustached Warbler. Background: Great Tit *Parus major*. 02.007.AB.05032.01

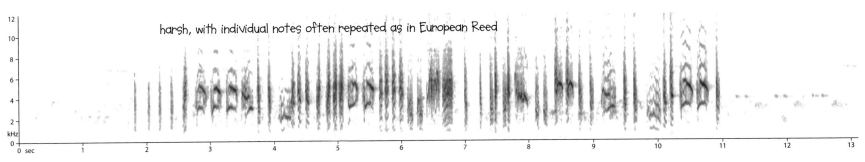

CD2-60 **Eastern (Saharan) Olivaceous Warbler** *Acrocephalus pallidus reiseri* Mareth, Gabès, Tunisia, 09:08, 1 May 2005. Song with harsh timbre and repetition of motifs several seconds long. Background: European Bee-eater *Merops apiaster* and Tunisian Chaffinch *Fringilla coelebs spodiogenys*. 05.006.AB.10516.11

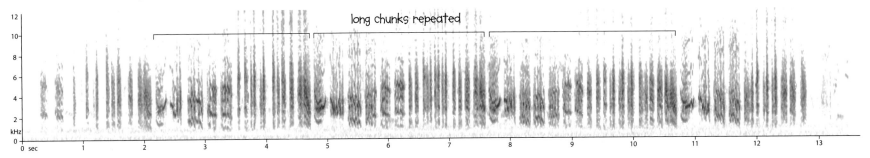

CD2-61 **Upcher's Warbler** *Hippolais languida* Wadi Dana, At Tafilah, Jordan, 1 May 2004. Song with mimicry (eg, of Red-rumped Swallow Cecropis *daurica*) and repetition of chunk of song up to four seconds long. Background: flock of Tristram's Grackles *Onychognathus tristramii* passing by. 04.015.MR.02537.01

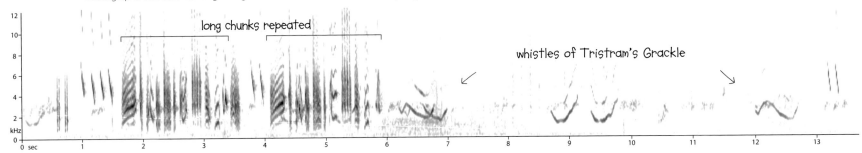

CD2-62 **Icterine Warbler** *Hippolais icterina* Schiermonnikoog, Friesland, Netherlands, 8 May 2003. Song with diagnostic squeaky timbre and mimicry (eg, of Eurasian Oystercatcher *Haematopus ostralegus* at 0:30, Red-backed Shrike *Lanius collurio* at 0:05 and 0:10 and Western Jackdaw *Corvus monedula* at 0:28). Background: Red-necked Grebe *Podiceps grisegena* (at 1:03), Common Redshank *Tringa totanus* and Willow Warbler *Phylloscopus trochilus*. 03.014.MR.11622.01

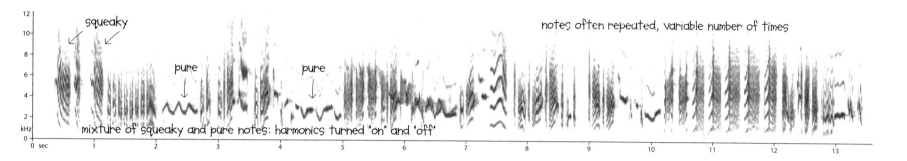

Here is another *Hippolais* song for you to listen to while making up your mind up **(CD2-62)**.

One *Acrocephalus* warbler we have kept out of the discussion so far is Cape Verde Warbler *A brevipennis*, an endemic Cape Verde Islands species occurring in the south-westernmost Western Palearctic **(CD2-63)**. It belongs to a group of African species called 'swamp warblers' that have different, bulbul-like songs. Indeed, on vocal characters, it seems less qualified to be a member of *Acrocephalus* than any of the 'tree warblers' (including *Hippolais*). Let's consider the main acro-points.

It can sing fairly continuously, but its streams of song are more broken up than in typical *Acrocephalus* songs, tending to consist of short, loud and varied trills, separated by gaps of roughly three seconds containing just a few quiet calls. The timbre of its song is not really harsh, nor is it pure and lyrical-sounding. Rather, it has a thrush-like, or better still bulbul-like quality, combining angular lines with a somewhat mellow timbre, sounding like the song of a larger bird. It is very much a daytime singer, although it has been heard to sing in the dark after rains (BWP). Cape Verde Warbler seems to be the only Western Palearctic *Acrocephalus* without mimicry of other species in its song, but it is possible that we have simply not detected it. Although it does repeat longer chunks of song, it does so with the repetitions separated by long gaps. It also has quite different calls and with its bulbul-like song, this species seems to fit rather uncomfortably in *Acrocephalus*, unlike the *Hippolais* warblers.

We have been unable to find any vocal characters that separate the 'hippos' cleanly from the 'acros'. *Hippolais*, on vocal characters at least, is a poorly defined genus. The Dutch committee for avian systematics (CSNA), whose taxonomy we follow in this book, was able to move only the four olivaceous and booted warblers, the so-called *Iduna* group, from *Hippolais* to *Acrocephalus*, because the DNA work their decision was based on did not look at all members of the traditional *Hippolais* group. Vocally, there seems to be nothing clearly separating the remaining *Hippolais* members from olivaceous and booted warblers (or *Acrocephalus*, for that matter).

Cape Verde Warbler *Acrocephalus brevipennis*, São Jorge de Orgãos, Santiago, Cape Verde Islands, 11 March 2004 *(Arnoud B van den Berg)*. Perhaps same bird as on CD2-63.

CD2-63   **Cape Verde Warbler** *Acrocephalus brevipennis* São Jorge de Orgãos, Santiago, Cape Verde Islands, 09:52, 11 March 2004. Song from dense vegetation in dry river bed. Background: Blackcap *Sylvia atricapilla*, Spanish Sparrow *Passer hispaniolensis* and Common Waxbill *Estrilda astrild*. 04.004.AB.04855.10

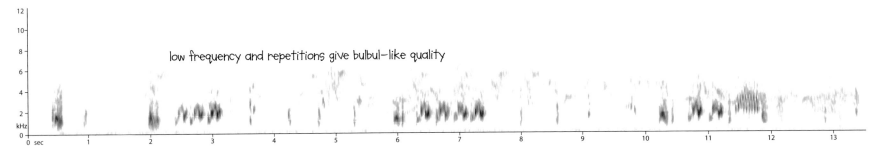

Crossbills and *The origin of species*

Jeff Groth first published his work on 'vocal types' of North American crossbills in 1988. It was and still is a shock. He described two populations of crossbills that differed strongly in their flight calls, excitement calls and alarm calls. In plumage they were identical, showing only slight but nevertheless significant differences in their measurements, especially the dimensions of the bill. These could later be explained as adaptations to foraging principally on spruce *Picea* in one, and pine *Pinus* in the other (eg, Groth 1993). Because they were breeding in the same Appalachian forests but maintained their distinctness, Groth argued for them being separate, 'cryptic' species. Later, his research across the whole continent, published in 1993, resulted in as many as eight of these new crossbills, and subsequently Craig Benkman (eg, 2003) discovered a locally endemic ninth one in the South Hills of Idaho, USA. In his North American bird guide, Sibley (2000) lists and describes these nine types as "possibly nine separate species". All are specialists at extracting seeds from a particular type of cone, and all differ slightly in measurements, though not in plumage. At one time it was suggested that vocal types involved dialects but, by definition, dialects are linked to a specific area; they might meet but they don't mix. In contrast, these nomadic vocal types overlap in their breeding distributions, not incidentally here and there, but as a matter of course over large areas of North America's coniferous forests.

When I was introduced to Magnus by Arnoud at the Dutch Birding annual meeting in February 1999, he had been up all night, making copies of a CD of crossbills recorded in Europe over the previous three years. Inspired by Groth's work, which had been summarised in Dutch Birding (Sangster 1996), he had recorded and analysed flight calls, excitement calls and alarm calls in the Netherlands and beyond, and was able to show that at least six additional vocal types of 'common crossbill' could be found in Europe. The sleeve notes explained that crossbills paired according to type, and that differences in calls were not a matter of age or sex. Wow! What were these birds, and where did they come from? How did they relate to Two-barred *L leucoptera*, Scottish *L scotica* and Parrot Crossbills *L pytyopsittacus*? And when and where would it be published? At that time, I seemed to be constantly explaining to various enthusiasts that they couldn't claim something was a separate species unless they had eliminated all other explanations. Yet Magnus was making no such claims; he just showed how it worked. I bought all the CDs, not wanting anyone to run away with his results before they had been published properly. The editors of Dutch Birding soon became aware of the work, and in spring 2000 the paper was published with a comprehensive audio CD comparing the six types of 'common' plus Two-barred, Scottish and Parrot Crossbills (Robb 2000).

In 2000, when we started The Sound Approach, Arnoud concentrated on recording regular species in mainland Europe, and I worked with Dick and Killian in Finland and Norway. Magnus specialised in visiting areas where endemics and 'new species' could be found. His adventures could fill another book, but one of the easier trips involved a visit to Canada especially to record the sounds of White-winged Crossbills *L l leucoptera*. We knew that this smaller North American version of the Two-barred Crossbill *L l bifasciata* of Eurasia had a finer bill, and a more contrasting plumage that included more black, especially on the lores and surrounding the ear coverts (Cramp & Perrins 1994).

Published recordings show that White-winged of both sexes, young and old, have a vocabulary of sounds very different from Two-barred. In many respects, White-winged seem closer to redpolls, the nearest relatives of crossbills (Arnaiz-Villena et al 2001). It is not difficult to distinguish between the various sounds of White-winged and Two-barred Crossbills. Listen for yourself (**CD2-64 to 69**). The wing-barred crossbills of North America and Eurasia seem to have diverged not only in song and calls, but also in ecology, measurements and plumage. Hispaniolan Crossbill *L megaplaga* of the Caribbean, another crossbill with wing bars, was recently split from *leucoptera* and *bifasciata* for similar reasons (Smith 1997, American

Ornithologists' Union 1998, Boon et al 2006) and for consistency, White-winged and Two-barred are probably also best treated as separate phylogenetic species.

Two-barred Crossbill *Loxia leucoptera bifasciata*, IJzeren Veld, Huizen, Noord-Holland, Netherlands, 2 February 2003 *(Arnoud B van den Berg)*. Foraging in larch trees. Same bird on the same day as on CD2-64 and 68.

CD2-64   **Two-barred Crossbill** *Loxia leucoptera bifasciata* Huizen, Noord-Holland, Netherlands, 2 February 2003. Song of an adult male. Background: Eurasian Siskin *Carduelis spinus* and Glip Crossbill *L c* type C. 02.046.MR.13952.02

CD2-65   **White-winged Crossbill** *Loxia leucoptera leucoptera* Algonquin Provincial Park, Ontario, Canada, 6 August 2000. Song of an adult male. Background: American Herring Gull *Larus smithsonianus*, Yellow-bellied Sapsucker *Sphyrapicus varius*, Olive-sided Flycatcher *Contopus cooperi*, Alder Flycatcher *Empidonax alnorum* and Green Frog *Rana clamitans*. 00.043.MR.02927.00

CD2-66   **Two-barred Crossbill** *Loxia leucoptera bifasciata* Baarn, Noord-Holland, Netherlands, 13 March 1998. **Flight calls** of a bird taking off. 98.31B.MR.00001.12

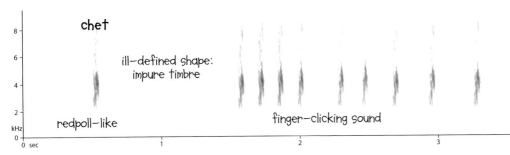

CD2-67   **White-winged Crossbill** *Loxia leucoptera leucoptera* Algonquin Provincial Park, Ontario, Canada, 7 August 2000. **Flight calls** of an adult male, up to and including take-off. Background: whistles of Gray Jay *Perisorius canadensis*. 00.044.MR.05645.00

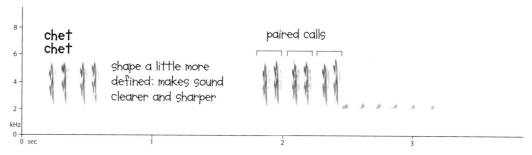

CD2-68   **Two-barred Crossbill** *Loxia leucoptera bifasciata* Huizen, Noord-Holland, Netherlands, 2 February 2003. **Trumpet or excitement calls** of an adult male. Background: Winter Wren *Troglodytes troglodytes*. 02.046.MR.14458a.02

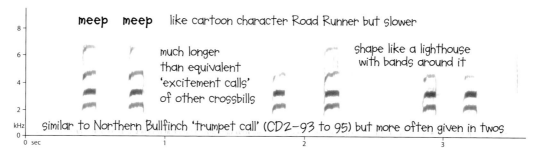

CD2-69   **White-winged Crossbill** *Loxia leucoptera leucoptera* Algonquin Provincial Park, Ontario, Canada, 6 August 2000. **Excitement calls** of an adult male. This call is equivalent to the trumpet calls of Two-barred Crossbill in function, despite sounding very different (Benkman 1992). 00.044.MR.01604.01

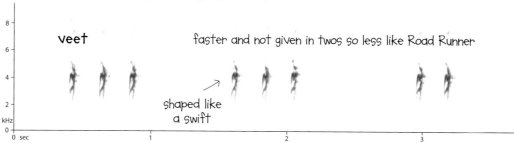

Although Dutch Birding had published the paper and CD, interest in the vocal types didn't really take off. Birders didn't realise how important it was to know the various sounds of the different vocal types if you were to accurately identify Two-barred Crossbill and Parrot Crossbill by call. In autumn 2002, migration watchers in the Netherlands started reporting a few Parrot Crossbills moving through the country. The apparent invasion gained support from observers at Falsterbo, the famous migration bottleneck at the southern tip of Sweden, who were reporting numbers of them passing through there too. At the same time, several ringers at different spots in the Netherlands, who were catching hundreds of birds, were unable to lend any credence to an invasion of Parrots: they didn't catch a single one, and an invasion of this species never did materialise that year. When Magnus went out in the hope of recording them at various local hotspots, he found 'common'-sized crossbills, giving a new flight call very similar to Parrot, but with excitement and alarm calls that were quite different. They became known as Parakeet Crossbill *L c* type X, so called because they sound like Parrot Crossbill but are smaller. They have been one of the commonest in the Netherlands since that time, and we have also recorded them in Poland and the UK.

Parakeet Crossbill isn't on the Dutch Birding CD, but in retrospect this is hardly surprising, because some of the six other crossbills which were around up to 1998 have been very scarce since. The only one which has remained equally widespread since 1998 is Glip Crossbill *L c* type C, named after the sound of its flight call. This highly mobile crossbill has been recorded in a variety of conifer species, from Finland to Spain, and in the UK from Shetland to Dorset, but seems to be particularly at home in Norway Spruce *Picea abies* forests in Scandinavia and the Alps.

Biometrics gathered from hundreds of sound recorded crossbills at four ringing sites in the Netherlands were unanimous on the average bill depth of these two crossbills. Contrary to any suggestions evoked by Parakeet's more powerful-sounding calls, Glip Crossbill actually has the deeper bill measurement (Edelaar et al 2004), albeit only by a few 10ths of a millimetre.

When you hear two clearly different calls from a flock of crossbills, you are not necessarily hearing two types. There are two commonly heard calls that are useful in identifying Crossbills: those made in or just before flight, and excitement calls.

Flight calls are *the* classic crossbill sound and are the first thing to learn. Some describe them as metallic, but no matter how much I bash two hammers together they don't sound that way to me. In fact the attempt to describe them accurately nearly had me hitting Magnus's head with the hammers. In true Mission Impossible style The Sound Approach called in Nick Hopper whose pragmatic approach to learning them was an inspiration. Between us all we found that the flight sounds varied between those that would be expected from a lost chick through to others that could be given by a passing Meadow Pipit *A pratensis*.

The different excitement calls are more subtle and sound superficially like a blackbird alarming at a cat but at various distances. They are more powerful, nasal and insistent than flight calls and typically sound lower-pitched, prompting fantasies of a bigger crossbill. Don't be fooled: all crossbills including Scottish and Parrot use them. In Two-barred the equivalent is the trumpet call. Essentially, there are calls for reinforcements, whether to mob an owl or just to liven up the party. They are highly infectious, and a translation would be something close to "here, here…". A good way to elicit excitement calls is to 'spish' quietly.

Not only is Glip Crossbill the commonest; it's also the one that has been used in the field guides, where its flight calls are described as a metallic *glip*. Crossbill excitement calls create another slight conflict as their sonagrams show a few strange phenomena. There are bands of sound within all but Glip and Scarce Crossbill *L c* type F excitement calls that provide a nasal quality but are not true harmonics. Glip Crossbill has none of these bands, only true harmonics. So although it's the most often described, its excitement calls are not typical. They sound rather like a falsetto version of the others. Compare the four sounds that you would be likely to hear from a mixed flock of Parakeet and Glip Crossbills (**CD2-70 to 73**). In my opinion Parakeet flight calls are like a lost chick while the corresponding sound from Glip is more like a sparrow. Parakeet's excitement call is very like a Common Blackbird. If this doesn't work for you, look carefully at the sonagrams and memorise them that way.

Parakeet Crossbill *Loxia curvirostra* type X, Kennemerduinen, Bloemendaal, Noord-Holland, Netherlands, 24 January 2006 *(Arnoud B van den Berg)*

Glip Crossbill *Loxia curvirostra* type C, Kennemerduinen, Bloemendaal, Noord-Holland, Netherlands, 2 September 2002 *(Arnoud B van den Berg)*

CD2-70   **Parakeet Crossbill** *Loxia curvirostra* type X, Kennemerduinen, Bloemendaal, Noord-Holland, Netherlands, 15:09, 15 November 2002. **Flight calls** of a ringed adult female, just after release. Background: Great Tit *Parus major* and Glip Crossbill *L c* type C. 02.033.AB.02545.02

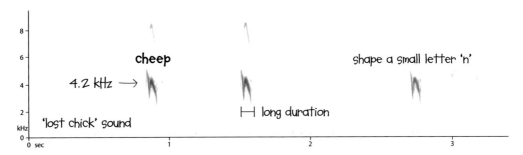

CD2-71   **Glip Crossbill** *Loxia curvirostra* type C, Kennemerduinen, Bloemendaal, Noord-Holland, Netherlands, 16 February 2002. **Flight calls** and wing *whirr* leading up to departure. 02.008.MR.04356.31

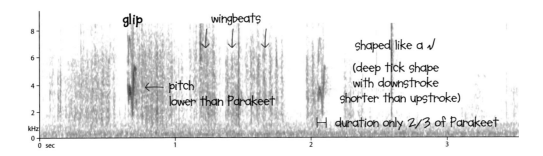

CD2-72   **Parakeet Crossbill** *Loxia curvirostra* type X, Taktom, Hanko, Uusimaa, Finland, 09:30, 10 March 2005. **Excitement calls** of several birds. Background: Great Tit *Parus major*, Crested Tit *Lophophanes cristatus* and distant Glip Crossbill *L c* type C. 05.001.DF.04154.02

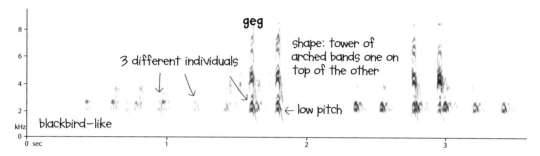

CD2-73   **Glip Crossbill** *Loxia curvirostra* type C, Kennemerduinen, Bloemendaal, Noord-Holland, Netherlands, 16 February 2002. **Excitement calls** of an adult male. Background: Eurasian Siskin *Carduelis spinus*. 02.008.MR.04731.01

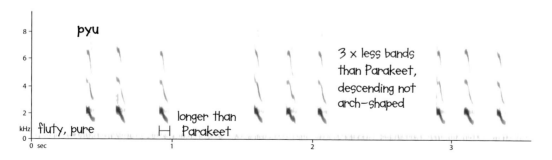

Wandering Crossbill *L c* type A is one of the more irruptive and widespread crossbills. It has a distinctive flight call, a short incisive, sharp *keep*, a bit like the *kip* of Arctic Tern or the contact *geg* sound Redwing makes when calling from a bush. Its excitement call is a fraction longer than the equivalent in Parakeet Crossbill, but sounds the same. Bohemian Crossbill *L c* type B has a diagnostic flight call, sounding like a passing Meadow Pipit. Its excitement call is higher pitched than most and has a hard and nasal quality. Bohemian seems to occur mainly in Black Pine *Pinus nigra* forests from Bohemia and the eastern Alps through the Balkans and into Turkey.

CD2-74   **Wandering Crossbill** *Loxia curvirostra* type A, Glenmore Forest Park, Highland, Scotland, 19 March 2002. **Flight calls** of a bird flying over the forest. Background: Goldcrest *Regulus regulus*. 02.010.MR.00018.12

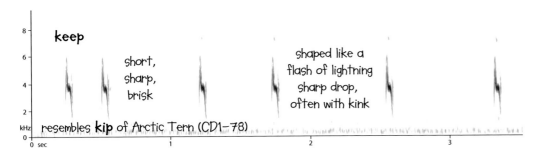

CD2-75   **Bohemian Crossbill** *Loxia curvirostra* type B, Soguksu national park, Ankara province, Turkey, 9 May 2001. **Flight calls** of a perched adult female, with quieter calls of a juvenile. Pitch can vary. Background: Common Blackbird *Turdus merula* and Common Chaffinch *Fringilla coelebs*. 01.018.MR.02417.11

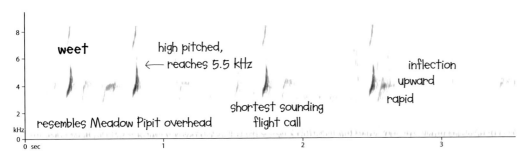

Wandering Crossbill *Loxia curvirostra* type A, Kennemerduinen, Bloemendaal, Noord-Holland, Netherlands, 13 February 1998 *(Arnoud B van den Berg)*

CD2-76 **Wandering Crossbill** *Loxia curvirostra* type A, Kennemerduinen, Bloemendaal, Noord-Holland, Netherlands, 16 February 2002. **Excitement calls**. Background: Winter Wren *Troglodytes troglodytes*, Brambling *Fringilla montifringilla* and Glip Crossbill *L c* type C. 02.008.MR.04357.11

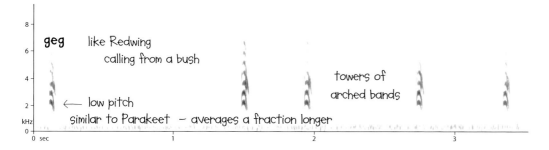

geg like Redwing calling from a bush

← low pitch

similar to Parakeet – averages a fraction longer

towers of arched bands

CD2-77 **Bohemian Crossbill** *Loxia curvirostra* type B, Grainau, Eibsee, Bayern, Germany, 17:59, 8 April 2003. **Excitement calls** and flight calls of three individuals, possibly in response to sound of a Eurasian Pygmy Owl. Background: Coal Tit *Periparus ater*. 03.005.AB.15809.11

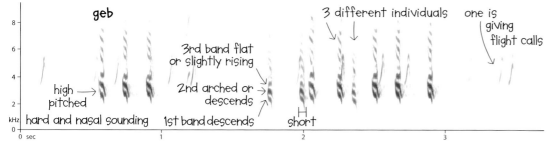

geb

3 different individuals

one is giving flight calls

3rd band flat or slightly rising

high → pitched

2nd arched or descends

hard and nasal sounding

1st band descends

short

Bohemian Crossbill *Loxia curvirostra* type B, Kennemerduinen, Bloemendaal, Noord-Holland, Netherlands, 13 February 1998 *(Arnoud B van den Berg)*

The next three crossbills can be identified by listening to both flight and excitement calls. This enables accurate identification every time. Phantom Crossbill *L c* type D, so called because it seems capable of disappearing for long periods then popping up unexpectedly, has so far only been recorded in the Benelux and southern England. It could well be missed purely because its flight calls are easily confused with Scarce Crossbill. Phantom's flight calls are reminiscent of redpoll flight calls while its excitement calls remind me of a Black-throated Thrush *T atrogularis* I once heard alarming at a Northern Goshawk.

British Crossbill *L c* type E is apparently the commonest crossbill in northern England and Scotland, especially in new plantations of North American conifers (only one flock has ever been recorded elsewhere, in 1997/98 on the Dutch coast). Its flight calls sound similar to Parakeet Crossbill's but its excitement calls are very different and remind me of a Western Jackdaw *C monedula*.

Flight calls of Scarce Crossbill are like Phantom Crossbill's but heavier and remind me of Common Chaffinch rain calls in southern Britain. Its excitement calls sound like Glip Crossbill's but more reminiscent of a Great Spotted Woodpecker *kit* note. No other crossbill combines these two calls. Scarce Crossbill has only been recorded in the Benelux, although it must also occur elsewhere as it was absent from the Benelux from 2001 until it turned up again in late 2005.

CD2-78   **Phantom Crossbill** *Loxia curvirostra* type D, Kennemerduinen, Bloemendaal, Noord-Holland, Netherlands, 28 March 2002. **Flight calls** of a perched adult male. Background: European Robin *Erithacus rubecula*, Common Chiffchaff *Phylloscopus collybita*, Common Chaffinch *Fringilla coelebs* and Eurasian Siskin *Carduelis spinus*. 02.011.MR.12642.22

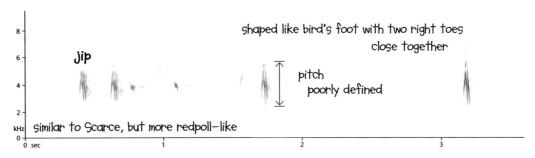

CD2-79   **British Crossbill** *Loxia curvirostra* type E, Kennemerduinen, Bloemendaal, Noord-Holland, Netherlands, 14 March 1998. **Flight calls** of a perched individual. 98.003.MR.03800.22

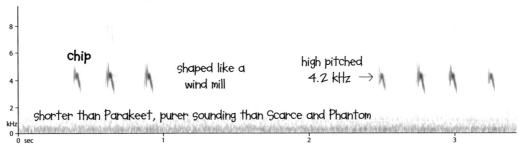

CD2-80   **Scarce Crossbill** *Loxia curvirostra* type F, Epe, Gelderland, Netherlands, 29 September 2001. **Flight calls** of a first-winter female held temporarily in captivity for ringing. Background: Marsh Tit *Poecile palustris* and Brambling *Fringilla montifringilla*. 01.039.MR.05507.01

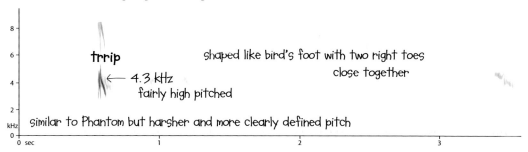

trrip

← 4.3 kHz
fairly high pitched

shaped like bird's foot with two right toes
close together

similar to Phantom but harsher and more clearly defined pitch

CD2-81   **Phantom Crossbill** *Loxia curvirostra* type D, Logbiermé, Liège, Belgium, 08:35, 22 April 2001. **Excitement calls**. Background: Mistle Thrush *Turdus viscivorus*, Firecrest *Regulus ignicapilla*, Coal Tit *Periparus ater* and Common Chaffinch *Fringilla coelebs*. 01.006.AB.10603.02

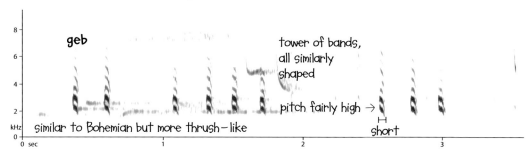

geb

tower of bands,
all similarly
shaped

pitch fairly high →

similar to Bohemian but more thrush-like

short

CD2-82   **British Crossbill** *Loxia curvirostra* type E, Ardgay, Highland, Scotland, 20 March 2002. **Excitement calls** of a male. 02.010.MR.03007.32

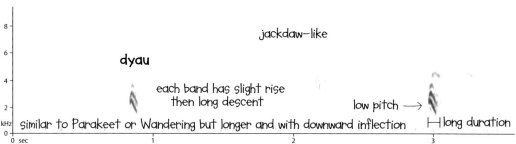

jackdaw-like

dyau

each band has slight rise
then long descent

low pitch →

similar to Parakeet or Wandering but longer and with downward inflection

long duration

Scarce Crossbill *Loxia curvirostra* type F, Baarn, Utrecht, Netherlands, 21 November 1999. **Excitement calls** of a male. 99.030.MR.10110.03

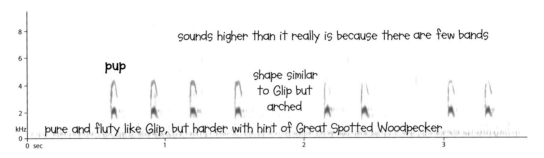

While learning the sounds of Scottish Crossbill, Magnus had studied previously published sonagrams (eg, BWP) and in March 1999, when he visited Abernethy forest, he recorded large-billed crossbills with similar calls for his Dutch Birding paper (Robb 2000). Sadly he wasn't in on one closely guarded secret; he didn't know that there were also large numbers of Parrot Crossbills in the Scottish Highlands. This put him at a considerable disadvantage and the sample of recordings that he published as Scottish Crossbill probably included *both* large-billed crossbill species.

Ron Summers is a researcher employed by the RSPB to study rare Scottish breeding species. An expert in crossbills he along with Craig Benkman, Mark Herremans, Alan Knox and myself were all sent the paper before publication for peer reviewing. None of us commented on the mistake.

Ron, David Jardine, Mick Marquiss and Rob Rae had been catching Parrot Crossbills between 1995 and 2000 and published their work on crossbill diversity in the Scottish Highlands in Ibis (Summers et al 2002). Through catching and ringing, Ron's team

had discovered that there were actually five crossbills occurring in Scotland including not only Scottish Crossbill but also considerable numbers of Parrot Crossbill. The secret was out, and Magnus's mistake was pointed out in their paper.

In their work, birds were measured and sorted into Scottish, Parrot and 'common'-sized, as well as being sound recorded. Summers and his co-workers developed their own system of classifying calls. Flight calls (four variants numbered 1 to 4) and excitement calls (five variants A to E) were considered separately, and these turned out to be used in consistent combinations: 1A was British, 2B was Wandering, 2D was Parrot, 3C was Scottish, and 4E was Glip. In addition to biometric and vocal data, Summers' team collected DNA samples, and this led to a startling discovery (Piertney et al 2001). None of these birds, not even Parrot Crossbill, seemed to be genetically distinct, meaning one of three things. Either they had evolved very recently, their genetic differences too subtle to be detected by the method used, or they were frequently hybridising species, or the different crossbills were not species but some kind of morphs, able to interbreed freely. The five crossbills in the Scottish

Highlands, occurring in the same mixture of native Scots Pine forests and non-native commercial plantations, all seem to be capable of retaining their distinctness; data collected in Scotland suggest that mixed pairs are extremely unusual (Summers pers comm). Such a situation is not unprecedented: it has proven equally difficult to find genetic support for the five redpolls *Carduelis* confidently identified by keen birders: Lesser *cabaret*, Mealy *flammea*, Greenland *rostrata*, Coues's Arctic *exilipes* and Hornemann's Redpolls *hornemanni*. Another parallel is the Galapagos finches discovered by Charles Darwin. When he visited the Galapagos Islands in 1835, these birds, with their amazing array of bill sizes for very specialised food sources, became one of the principle inspirations for *The origin of species* (1859). Galapagos finches are among the most closely studied birds in the world, and they also differ from each other in ecology, calls and songs. More than 100 years later, their evolution has actually been witnessed taking place (Weiner 1995), and yet their genes have proven to be an equally murky pool.

Now the secret was out, Magnus returned to Scotland to record birds for The Sound Approach. Staying with Ron, he was taken to some of the best sites. Parrot Crossbills aren't easy to record, and after several trips to Finland to capture them, Dick and I spent a desultory week in 2005 deep in the snow, trying to record them on the Finnish/Russian border with only one sighting. What we have now worked out is that flight calls of Parrots are quite variable. They differed for example between the 1983 and 1991 invasions in the Netherlands, although importantly, Parrot excitement calls were in all cases the same.

Describing the differences between Scottish and Parrot Crossbill's sounds **(CD2-84 to 87)** is like describing a malt whisky. The diagnostic Scottish excitement calls have a musical doubled note quality that, in true Scottish whisky salesman language, is peaty with more than a hint of a bee-eater flight call about it. Meanwhile, Parrot's excitement calls remind me of the same salesman tapping out his receipt on an old fashioned typewriter.

Parrot Crossbill *Loxia pytyopsittacus*, Koningshof, Overveen, Noord-Holland, Netherlands, 17 January 1991 *(Arnoud B van den Berg)*

CD2-84   **Parrot Crossbill** *Loxia pytyopsittacus* Abernethy forest, Highland, Scotland, 19 March 2002. **Flight calls** of an adult male close to a nest where the pair had already been measured and ringed. Background: Common Chaffinch *Fringilla coelebs*. 02.010.MR.00222.20

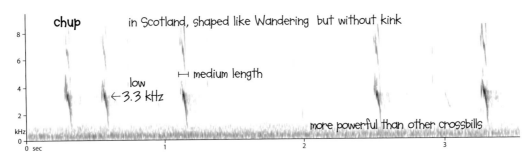

CD2-85   **Scottish Crossbill** *Loxia scotica* Ardgay, Highland, Scotland, 20 March 2002. **Flight calls** of a pair, ending with their departure. 02.010.MR.04825.11

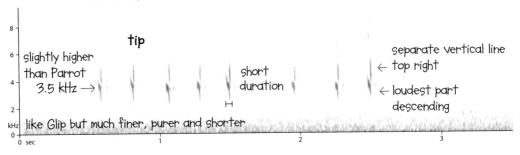

CD2-86   **Parrot Crossbill** *Loxia pytyopsittacus* Abernethy forest, Highland, Scotland, 19 July 2001. **Excitement calls** of several males and females. Background: juvenile Common Buzzard *Buteo buteo*, Crested Tit *Lophophanes cristatus*, Coal Tit Periparus ater, Eurasian Treecreeper *Certhia familiaris* and Common Chaffinch *Fringilla coelebs*. 01.035.MR.01123.01

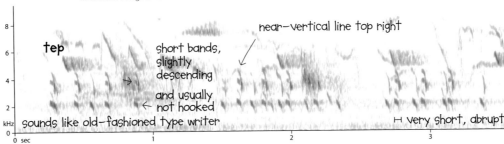

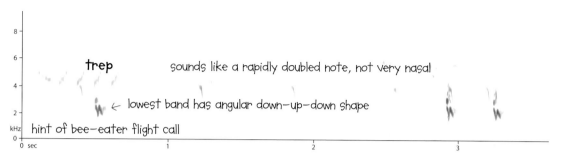

CD2-87   **Scottish Crossbill** *Loxia scotica* Ardgay, Highland, Scotland, 20 March 2002. **Excitement calls** and quiet flight calls of a pair near their nest. Background: Eurasian Skylark *Alauda arvensis*, Winter Wren *Troglodytes troglodytes*, European Robin *Erithacus rubecula* and Song Thrush *Turdus philomelos*. 02.010.MR.03323.01

So where does this leave Scottish and Parrot Crossbills? Really keen twitchers like Lee Evans struggle to know what can and cannot be ticked. Lee is a chronicler of twitching lore and only trusts his eye when identifying birds. This book however is primarily about sounds, not taxonomy, so thankfully we don't need to decide here and now whether to give all those crossbills 'species' labels. Several teams are analysing them in various different ways that will eventually resolve their status; European work in progress is summarised in Edelaar et al (2003). Using a new technique, a team in North America has found small but significant genetic differences between the vocal types of crossbill there (Parchman et al 2006), and it seems likely that this can be done in Europe as well. The crucial point to understand in the meantime is this: that all these plain-winged crossbills are in the same boat. Scottish and Parrot Crossbills just happen to be the largest, which allowed them to be discovered early on, back in the days when only silent, dead birds in museums were studied in any detail.

So for Lee and those wondering where this leaves the crossbills' status as species? Galapagos finches are far too high profile to be left in this species' no-man's land and scientists are already debating their status (Zink 2002). In the same way crossbills' status will be decided. Meanwhile sound as a primary means of determining species is starting to come back into its own and vocally distinct populations of crossbills exist. So, when you are birding in the UK, it is best to start sorting out British from Scottish Crossbills.

Part 9: Playback and be damned

Interacting with birds: imitating, whistling and spishing

Much of what we have summarised in the second half of this book was researched by scientists playing sounds to birds and observing their response, a technique called *playback*. Birders, and especially bird tour leaders, sometimes use pre-recorded sounds or record an unseen bird and play its own sound back to it, hoping to bring the bird closer. This is also called playback or, more commonly, tape-luring. The technique has a chequered reputation, and at worst it is used by bird-catchers in countries like Cyprus to draw birds to their death.

Ringers regularly use playback to attract birds into their nets, and many ringing stations, especially in the Benelux countries, are arrayed with speakers pointing at the stars. Vagrants are sometimes tape-lured with song in an attempt to confirm their identification. Nearly all bird tour leaders will use it now and then hoping to show a highly sought-after bird to a holidaying group of birders as quickly as they can. Photographers sometimes use tape-luring in order to bring their subjects close, and they often betrayed themselves with images of over-excited birds. The effectiveness can vary enormously and Arnoud, when leading tours, believes that its success depends on the species and time of year. When tried in September in Morocco, it only works less than 10% of the time, whereas in Holland a Water Rail, Willow Tit or Short-toed Treecreeper will respond to Arnoud's efforts at any time of year. Some sound recordists use it to improve their recordings, although in The Sound Approach database of 30 000 recordings, only 125 were tape-lured. In this publication, only the four mentioned below were lured, and not all by playback as we shall see.

Many birders consider playback distasteful on aesthetic grounds, especially if it is loud, wanting to enjoy peaceful surroundings, and natural sights and sounds. Others see it as sloppy technique or indeed cheating, like athletes secretly resorting to the use of steroids, but the most frequently voiced objections concern possible effects on the birds themselves. These usually suggest that birds desert territories, nests, or young, become an easy target for predators by getting in the open, or suffer long term stress, having been humiliated by a much louder competitor (the playback). It's worth mentioning at this point that in many countries, interacting with a locally rare bird could contravene the law.

For scientists, however, playback has been used as an important experimental technique in thousands of field experiments, apparently without any of these negative effects. It is thought that when playback is used in a male bird's territory the main effect is to raise his testosterone levels. Research has shown that when the song of a given species is played in an area where there are several territories, males will usually be concerned about another male fertilising their mate (Dabelsteen & McGregor 1996). Most songbirds are promiscuous, and when

Black Woodpecker *Dryocopus martius*, female, flying overhead after being whistled in, Hanko, Uussima, Finland, October 2005 *(Dick Forsman)*

you play a song inside a pair's territory you are behaving in a pretty insolent way. The male has various ways to respond to any interloper. He can stay silent close to the female, and research shows that when she is about to ovulate this is the normal strategy. Alternatively, he can fly towards the sound, singing or calling, and try to drive the newcomer from his territory. He will judge the distance to the intruder, and therefore the seriousness of the intrusion, by the degree of degradation of the sound, *not by loudness*. He will recognise whether the intruder is a neighbour by listening for any shared songs. A female may also be drawn to the newcomer in the hope of an extra-pair copulation, although research shows that females tend to be more discerning than males, so they are less easily fooled by playback. In natural circumstances, an unfamiliar, opportunistic challenger will tend to be a less experienced first-year male. If this is so, a resident male may be sufficiently emboldened to chase off the youngster, and a female will generally be less attracted to him.

Magnus experienced another aspect of tape-luring on the 8th of August 2004 while looking for migrant Aquatic Warblers in his patch at Kennemermeer near IJmuiden, the sea harbour 25 km west of Amsterdam. Setting off to look for one that had been found the day before, he was still 80 m from some other birders when he noticed a juvenile singing right beside him (**CD2-88**). Although he had seen quite a few juvenile Aquatics at this site before, this was the only time he had ever heard one singing. When the other birders joined him, it turned out that they had been playing an Aquatic tape, trying to lure another individual. So, their tape had the desired effect of bringing an Aquatic up out of the sedges and even stimulated it to sing. However, they had not noticed this because this happened too far from where

they had been playing the sound. Shaun Robson experienced a similar situation when he and Bob Gifford were ringing in Shaun's patch of Lytchett Bay in Poole. They had been using a tape to bring birds to the nets and having packed everything away were leaving the ringing site when they heard an Aquatic singing. Not believing his ears Shaun immediately thought I was hiding in the reeds playing a tape. In fact he still thinks this. As in much adult song of this species, the subsong in this recording is very simple and consists mainly of *trrt* notes. Without hearing the fine warbling between these notes, mainly heard later in the recording, one could be forgiven for dismissing the recording as a series of calls.

Aquatic Warbler *Acrocephalus paludicola* IJmuiden, Noord-Holland, Netherlands, 08:00, 8 August 2004. Subsong of a juvenile that had been tape-lured by birders 80 m away. Background: begging calls of juvenile Common Reed Bunting *Emberiza schoeniclus*. 04.039.MR.14040.12

CD2-88

When he lured a male Black Woodpecker *Dryocopus martius* in the French Pyrenees, Arnoud used playback of a pre-recorded male's song. Our bird flew in and sized us up from behind a nearby tree trunk but did not call, and after looking around it eventually flew off. As we then made our way through the woods some way from the original bird, we heard several male Black Woodpeckers calling and drumming. You can hear at least three of them in **CD2-89**. They had been quiet before, but now this displaying went on for hours.

Black Woodpecker *Dryocopus martius* Col de Spandelles, Hautes-Pyrénées, France, 15:34, 18 June 2002. Quiet drumming, and laughing song of a male at close range, answered by at least two distant birds. Background: Common Chiffchaff *Phylloscopus collybita* and Common Chaffinch *Fringilla coelebs*. 02.022.AB.10410b.11

CD2-89

This kind of reaction was described by S J Gray (in McGregor & Dabelsteen 1996). In his studies of male Zitting Cisticolas, Gray noticed that while these birds listened during playback sessions their neighbours were engaged in, they decreased their own vocal activity by 53%, and after playback stopped they increased it by 254% in an effort to stop the apparent interloper visiting their territories. Eavesdropping by pairs nearby can mean that playback has a ripple effect, resulting in more vocal activity across several territories.

Give a little whistle

Bird sounds are an aspect of behaviour, and we have to be very sharp observers if we want to achieve anything with them. This applies just as much whether we are trying to attract birds, or simply to identify them. Researchers, who can spend a lifetime studying their subjects, get to know exactly how they behave. Birders on the other hand tend to use playback in a rather haphazard way. This is less exact, often embarrassingly clumsy, and typically unsuccessful. If you impersonate bird calls instead, either by whistling or by using a bird whistle or other instrument, you can be more sensitive, and possibly more successful. Returning to Black Woodpecker, Dick often whistles them in by impersonating the male's song (**CD2-90**). This usually works, and his tour groups are often astonished to see one hurtling towards them from a considerable distance. If you compare Dick's imitation with the song of a real Black Woodpecker in the preceding track, you can hear that not only has Dick got the changes in speed and pitch right; he also waits about 25 seconds before doing his next series, just like a real Black Woodpecker.

Dick Forsman *Homo sapiens* Tvärminne, Hanko, Uusimaa, Finland, 27 March 2005. Dick whistles his imitation of a Black Woodpecker *Dryocopus martius* song. In this instance, there were two males squaring off on opposite sides of a nearby trunk (you can hear some very quiet calls and their claws scratching the bark), and Dick was trying to break the stalemate. Background: excitement calls of distant Glip Crossbills *Loxia curvirostra* type C. 05.001.DF.12339.10   CD2-90

TV and radio personality Percy Edwards could impersonate hundreds of birds (he also provided the voice of the alien in the film *The Alien*), and he used a variety of techniques to attract curious birds. He would whistle a bird's song to get it to show itself, and sometimes use gentle tutting to decoy wheatears, stonechats, redstarts, flycatchers and others. By making a kissing sound by putting two fingers across his mouth and sucking, he also attracted inquisitive birds (Edwards & Watson 1986).

Pekka Pouttu (right) teaching Killian Mullarney how to do an imitation of a Northern Goshawk *Accipiter gentilis*, Hauho, Kanta-Häme, Finland, 31 March 2002 *(Mark Constantine)*. Same sound source as on CD2-91.

Pekka Pouttu *Homo sapiens* Hauho, Kanta-Häme, Finland, 31 March 2002. Pekka does an amazing imitation of a Northern Goshawk *Accipiter gentilis*, prompting responses from a male Northern Bullfinch *Pyrrhula pyrrhula pyrrhula*. In addition: *chick-a-dee* type calls of Great Tit *Parus major*, song of Eurasian Treecreeper *Certhia familiaris*, calls of distant Hooded Crows *Corvus cornix* and Yellowhammer *Emberiza citrinella*. 02.006.MC.00820.31

Pekka Pouttu is a sort of Percy Edwards of the Finnish forest, and like so many Finns he has a homemade owl-caller. He happily imitates Ural Owls, and attracts Eurasian Pygmy Owls by impersonating Tengmalm's Owls *Aegolius funereus*. Here, using a leaf, Pekka does an amazing impersonation of a Northern Goshawk, which stimulates a Northern Bullfinch *Pyrrhula pyrrhula pyrrhula* to call (**CD2-91**).

This kind of backwoodsmanship is also used widely in North America. Imitations of Eastern Screech-Owl *O asio* and Barred Owl *S varia* are so common during birdraces that it is a challenge not to tick another team by mistake. Another facet of attracting birds, especially in North America, is *spishing* or *pishing*. Often very effective, it involves making *psssh psssh psssh* sounds reminiscent of the calls of some birds when mobbing a predator.

Bruce Mactavish, 'Macspish' to his friends, is an exponent with a famed ability to attract flocks of small passerines while hiding deep in the bushes. Bruce has also shown me that spishing can be equally effective on both sides of the Atlantic. In fact, many exciting rarities have been found in this way. Ireland's second

Hume's Leaf Warbler *Phylloscopus humei*, Hook Head, Wexford, Ireland, 28 December 2003 *(Killian Mullarney)*. Same bird as on CD2-92.

CD2-92 **Hume's Leaf Warbler** *Phylloscopus humei* Hook Head, Wexford, Ireland, 15:50, 28 December 2003. Calls given by a vagrant in response to spishing. 03.017.KM.01855.22

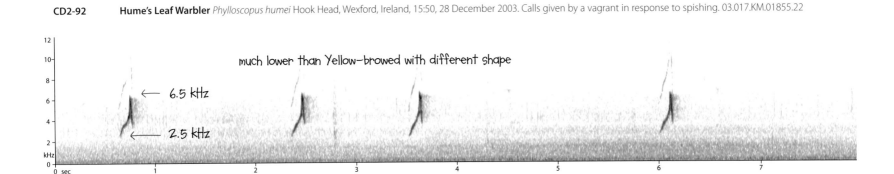

Hume's Leaf Warbler *P humei* was found by Killian on Hook Head, Ireland, while spishing opportunistically at a series of bushes **(CD2-92)**.

While I was travelling with Dick in Spain, we met an old friend, Gordon Wilson, who was on a birding holiday with a large group of his friends, some of whom were very keen to see a European Scops Owl. They had been trying playback without success for several evenings and wondered if we could help. We listened to their scops owl playback which, due to the tape copy, the machine itself or the speakers, was dreadful. After some debate we all drove off into the countryside, parked in a suitable spot, and Dick whistled the typical monotone song of a scops owl. Within a very short time he was engaged in a duet, answering back and forth.

It seems that the secret for successfully drawing birds towards you is to have experience of the way they use their vocabulary, and to listen carefully for any reaction. I often record with the help of a friend, so that one of us can do the recording while the other confirms the identity, age, sex and behaviour of the subject. When recording, it can be all too easy to lose perspective, and focus too much on operating the equipment. I think it can be the same with playback: by the time you have got the equipment working, set up the speakers, and found the right place on the tape, CD or mp3 player, you are no longer listening carefully to the interaction.

To sum up, whether you lure with playback, your voice or a whistle, consider what part of a bird's repertoire you are using, and don't go on for too long. If a bird doesn't respond fairly quickly, try returning once or twice later that day or the next. This

enables you to get the benefit of the priming process you have started (Smith 1996). The stimulated bird may sing more within a few hours as his hormone levels rise. At a shorter time scale, many species will search silently once the sound has stopped and will continue looking for up to half an hour, so using more than three or four phrases of playback is not necessary. If a bird sings in response, it will probably start to increase the pace of its songs and turn to face you. Birds often match the song you are producing, and may sing a simplified male-to-male variant of their song, lacking any female-attracting adornments. If you are already close, they may sing more faintly or approach silently. Females are more likely to be excited by impersonations than be led to desert their nests, although they will probably ignore it. Good quality sound is likely to be more effective than loudness, which just annoys other birders and gets in the way of listening. And bear in mind that the male to which the recording is being played may be less likely to sing back than his neighbours.

When actually tape-luring, basic procedure is to play two or more song types for a short time at least 20 m away from where the subject is expected to be at a volume that would sound natural at that distance. Remember that the bird is listening for degradation not loudness, and a poor loudspeaker or badly copied recording could degrade the sound beyond recognition. Try to emulate a natural intrusion into a territory: make sure the gaps between songs are as natural as possible (commercial recordings other than our own often have silences edited to save space), and if you have them, use songs of first-year males. Position the sound source near vegetation that could hide an intruder and if unsuccessful try again at a spot a little closer. If, having primed the birds, you still have no luck in drawing one into view, search the surrounding area, looking and listening for the silent male or his neighbours. If you have to come back later, don't forget to listen for a while before you do any playback.

Bird song is a government indicator of quality of life in Britain (DETR 2001) and you would imagine that it's either something that you are either blessed with in your area or not. This isn't the case. When I first started visiting Mallorca there was little to no dawn chorus. Thrushes were shot in the winter for food and became rarities by springtime. At dawn in the countryside around Pollensa, Stone-curlew would join the cockerels and that would be it. Now, blackbirds, robins, rock thrushes *Monticola* and other chats all contribute to a reasonable dawn chorus. Back home, in the winter, I feed over 20 Common Blackbirds in my garden along with half a dozen Blackcaps and a host of other birds. At the time of writing (February) I have robins, blackbirds and Song Thrushes *T philomelos* singing, and Blackcap subsinging each morning. Further up and down the road there is no singing this early in the year. Birds have more time to sing when they need less time for foraging. They can also attract a mate earlier if they are well-fed and strong, and when a good source of food is nearby.

Part 10: The sound approach to birding

When I imagine my name in British Birds ('BB'), I always see it after the words 'White's Thrush 17th October, Studland village' so, 'M Constantine pers comm', in Pennington & Meek's (2006) paper on 'The Northern Bullfinch invasion of Autumn 2004' wasn't quite what I wanted. Particularly because I couldn't remember communicating with either of the authors, although as it turned out, Arnoud had told them about a Northern Bullfinch I recorded in Finland. I wish I had been in contact with the authors directly, as it is an interesting paper, discussing an unknown 'trumpeting' call which was picked up all over Europe. There's a single page on sound, where the distinctive call is discussed at length and then a three-page discussion at the end, all best summed up by the authors echoing previous brave souls who tried to write about bird sounds: "the wide range of descriptions and comparisons used by observers only served to emphasise the variations in human perception".

Pennington and Meek ask the following questions. Where have the birds making this call come from? Why had so many of those that they had corresponded with never, or only occasionally, heard the distinctive trumpet call before? Was the sound diagnostic of Northern Bullfinch? They concluded that "this call is not diagnostic of Northern Bullfinch", "that birds giving such a call had been recorded in northern and western Europe before", and that the birds most likely originated in European Russia, with any heard further west in the breeding season "possibly lingering from previous influxes". What makes the piece most interesting is that it illustrates so well the problems of investigating puzzles like this without a framework to make sense of the sounds. To conclude the book lets try to answer the same questions using 'The Sound Approach to birding'.

We are more fortunate than they because we can start with an unequivocal example of a known Northern Bullfinch making the sound that everyone is talking about. On the 1st of November 2004, Arnoud recorded a first-year female Northern Bullfinch at the ringing station in the Kennemerduinen national park near his home in the Netherlands (**CD2-93**). It had been measured and identified to subspecies, ringed, photographed and released, and was calling three metres up in a dead tree, six metres away from him. We can see from the frequency of this call in the sonagram that it's perfectly within normal hearing limits, so it's not being misheard. If birders were missing them in the past, this had more to do with not listening out for them, rather than the sound being missed. We know that the same sound is used in flight, because we have a recording of calls of another female

'Trumpeting' Northern Bullfinch *Pyrrhula pyrrhula pyrrhula* and (at right) 'European' Bullfinch *P p europoea*, male, trapped at bird ringing station Van Lennep, Kennemerduinen, Bloemendaal, Noord-Holland, Netherlands, 1 November 2004 *(Arnoud B van den Berg/Vrs Van Lennep)*. Trapped at same site and at same moment as female of CD2-93.

(CD2-94) as it migrated along the Dutch coast, passing within a few metres. As we have demonstrated, there is nothing unusual in a bird using the same sound in different circumstances. Both birds were recorded in quite favourable acoustics, with negligible degradation of the sound at such short distances. If you listen carefully you can hear a slight Doppler effect as the migrating bird flies past the mic.

Northern Bullfinch *Pyrrhula pyrrhula pyrrhula*, first-winter female, 'trumpeting', Kennemerduinen, Bloemendaal, Noord-Holland, Netherlands, 1 November 2004 *(Arnoud B van den Berg/Vrs Van Lennep)*. Same 'trumpeting' bird as on CD2-93.

CD2-93   **Northern Bullfinch** *Pyrrhula pyrrhula pyrrhula* Kennemerduinen, Bloemendaal, Noord-Holland, Netherlands, 13:19, 1 November 2004. 'Trumpet' calls of a first-winter female perched on a 3 m high dead tree, shortly after release from ringing. Background: tapping Great Spotted Woodpecker *Dendrocopos major* and Wood Lark *Lullula arborea*. 04.024.AB.01348.01

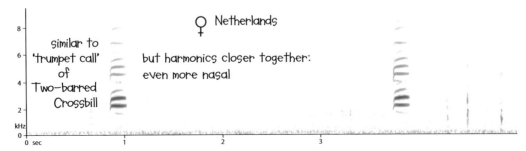

Now we have to consider ageing and sexing, as a first-year female may well sound different to an adult male. We can check this with a recording made at a migration hotspot in Sweden, where we recorded this male Northern Bullfinch perched on top of a tree (**CD2-95**) making a very similar sound to what we heard in the previous two recordings. In the collection, we also have other recordings of Northern Bullfinch of both sexes giving these calls, both first-years and adults.

By now it becomes clear that having real recordings to listen to and discuss is much more fruitful than having to guess the sound from comparisons such a "phone ringtone", a "far-away train horn" or a "rather electronic version of a car horn". The 'trumpet call' has a most distinctive tone, and is quickly distinguished from calls commonly produced by smaller Eurasian Bullfinch subspecies. The 'classic' bullfinch sound for western European ears is typified by equivalent calls of *pileata* of Britain and Ireland

CD2-94   **Northern Bullfinch** *Pyrrhula pyrrhula pyrrhula* Migration watchpoint Nolledijk, Vlissingen, Zeeland, Netherlands, 10:50, 8 November 2005. 'Trumpet' calls of a female migrating with Brambling *Fringilla montifringilla*. Background: Common Blackbird *Turdus merula*. 05.030.MR.12106.11

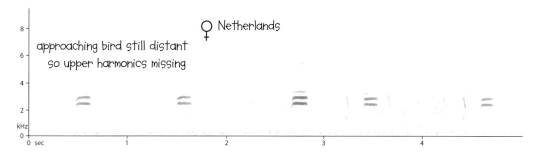

CD2-95   **Northern Bullfinch** *Pyrrhula pyrrhula pyrrhula* Torö island, Södermansland, Sweden, 19 November 2004. Calls of a male perched in a tree top, then flying off. 04.044.MR.00247.11

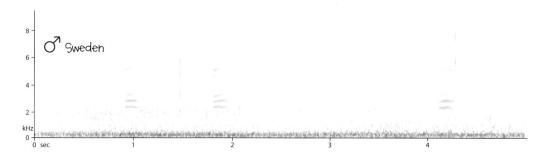

(CD2-96a), but note that *europoea* of western central Europe can have different and rather distinctive calls for flight and maintaining contact (CD2-96b), at least in coastal areas of the Netherlands. Comparing sonagrams, we learn that not only do these calls sound distinctively different; they also have quite different structures (the BB paper had no sonagrams).

Next, let's consider rhythm and timing. Northern Bullfinch 'trumpet calls' are sometimes used in stereotyped combinations with one or more other types of call. In CD2-97, doubled calls very similar to trumpet calls alternate with two other types of buzzing notes in a regular sequence. Bullfinches of both sexes are known to produce these 'sequence calls', and our collection reveals that they can be heard at various times of the year. The

CD2-96a   **'British' Bullfinch** *Pyrrhula pyrrhula pileata* Murrintown, Wexford, Ireland, 12 December 2004. Typical calls
0:00 – 0:10   of a bird flying past. 05.001.KM.00150.22

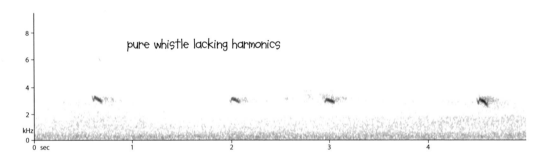

CD2-96b   **'European' Bullfinch** *Pyrrhula pyrrhula europoea* IJmuiden, Noord-Holland, Netherlands, 09:20, 27
0:12 – 0:31   October 2005. Flock of five migrating along the Dutch coast. Background: Meadow Pipit *Anthus pratensis*, Dunnock *Prunella modularis*, European Robin *Erithacus rubecula* and Western Jackdaw *Corvus monedula*. 05.028.MR.00628.02

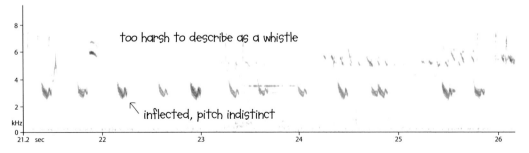

repeated nature of 'sequence calls', given by perched, often solitary bullfinches of all subspecies, suggests a parallel with chaffinch 'rain calls', reminding us of the possibility that what we thought was a call may sometimes be used as part of a song.

When reading the BB paper, you get the uneasy feeling that the authors and most of their correspondents assumed that Northern Bullfinches have just one or two calls, rather than a whole repertoire of sounds that can be used in many ways. Listen to a couple of other calls in the non-breeding repertoire of Northern Bullfinch **(CD2-98)**. BWP lists 17 types of call and song, with extensive notes on the behavioural context in which they have been heard.

CD2-97 **Northern Bullfinch** *Pyrrhula pyrrhula pyrrhula* Hauho, Kanta-Häme, Finland, 31 March 2002. Sequence calls heard in response to a Eurasian Pygmy Owl and a whistle used to lure it. Background: several other Northern Bullfinches, including some quiet song; also Hooded Crow *Corvus cornix*, Common Chaffinch *Fringilla coelebs* and Yellowhammer *Emberiza citrinella*. 02.003.KM.01800.12

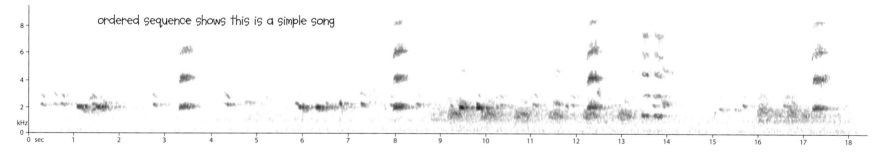

CD2-98 **Northern Bullfinch** *Pyrrhula pyrrhula pyrrhula* Torö island, Södermansland, Sweden, 19 November 2004. Two males and two females; one gives *tip* calls until it takes off (a normal context for this call, which may be equivalent to flight calls of crossbills). As this bird takes off, three calls of a second type are heard, then several 'trumpet calls' of a bird that stays perched, the last four of which are rather loud. 04.043.MR.20304.01

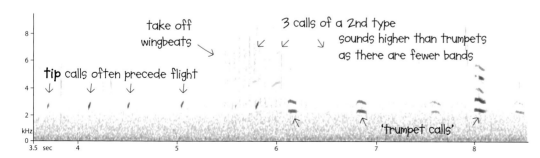

Interesting though these other calls are, as birders we know that we can often identify birds quite successfully when we just know one of their sounds. This works because outside the breeding season, and especially in winter conditions, most birds only use a small part of their total repertoire. Sexual attraction, rivalries and caring for young are no longer the main issues; the priority is to stay with friends and keep out of danger. At such times, birds behave less extravagantly to conserve energy. A much smaller repertoire of calls fulfills their needs, and certain calls will now be used much more often. This may be one reason why the 'trumpet calls' of Northern Bullfinches attract our attention during migration and winter. Listening to and analysing our own recordings of Northern Bullfinches made in Finland and Lapland from 2001 to the present, and to Finnish sound publications like Luonto Soi (Hallikainen 2001) and Lintumme Laulavat (Birdlife Finland 2001) we find that in some areas the 'trumpet call' is used throughout the year although during the breeding season it probably forms a smaller part of the total vocal output. So if Finland and Lapland form part of the normal range of 'trumpeter bullfinches', why were so few Finnish birders familiar with these calls? Who knows, but having been on three winter recording trips to Finland, in temperatures as low as -18°C, I can tell you that even hardened Finns wearing three layers of thermal underwear don't like to stay outside too long in the winter.

At this stage we can sum up a couple of our conclusions. Although we have no reason to dispute that the 'trumpet call' is used by Northern Bullfinches from further east (Antero Lindholm has recorded 'trumpeters' in Komi, European Russia), it appears that this sound is used regularly by Finnish birds, and its occurrence seems too widespread to be explained by birds "possibly lingering from previous influxes". We would agree that

it had been noticed before 2004, as we had previously recorded it ourselves, both in Finland and during autumn migration in the Netherlands. As to whether this sound is diagnostic for Northern Bullfinch, we have listened to and analysed many Eurasian Bullfinches of other subspecies, and we have yet to find it outside this taxon. So while we would agree that not every Northern Bullfinch uses this call, other bullfinches don't. In other words it *is* diagnostic.

However, as always, it's not quite that simple: now we need to bring a little caveat into the discussion. One of the features of Northern Bullfinches that made them very popular with bird keepers in the past is that they can be taught to mimic other sounds very easily. Ludwig Koch, in his *Encyclopedia of British birds* (1957), wrote that Northern Bullfinch was imported into England as a cage bird and that "this is the bullfinch seen for sale in shops". Northern Bullfinches were regularly taught to sing complicated songs with the help of a musical box or penny whistle. Research has also shown that bullfinches learn their calls from their father, and Bergmann & Helb (1982) tell us that parent bullfinches can also pass on songs learned from humans to their young. As in certain other finch species, it has also been discovered that individual pairs of bullfinch share their own distinctive calls; a bird can pick out and respond to its mate in among a crowd of others. So while the 'trumpet call' seems to be diagnostic of Northern, other bullfinches are probably capable of learning it.

Conclusion

This book is dedicated to Peter Grant. I first met him in Mallorca where he was tour leading. He was chairman of the British Birds Rarities Committee at the time and an editor of British Birds. I was very keen to learn, and he was a great teacher. After his tour leading duties, he would sit with Mo and me drinking wine and teach us about moult, topography, and identification. Through him I came to meet Killian, Arnoud and indirectly Magnus. This book was to be a pamphlet like his *The New Approach*, and through his example I looked and listened to bird sound and read the science behind it as in the same way he had approached gulls. He died of cancer at Easter in 1990, and as I conclude the book I am again in Mallorca and it is Easter 2006.

It could have as easily been dedicated to Magnus Robb, as the power house of The Sound Approach, had he not had so many accolades throughout this publication. Sometimes when he's deeply immersed in sound recording, I think he models himself on Orpheus, poet and musician, who protected the Argonauts from the Sirens with his music. According to myth, Orpheus taught the birds to sing, but Magnus, who thinks about such deep things, believes that the ancient Greeks got it the wrong way round, and the birds taught us to sing. Personally, sitting in these mountains puzzling over the differences between songs of both rock thrushes, I realise that the birds are teaching me to listen.

To conclude, see if you can hear Magnus sigh as nature tries to disrupt his efforts to record a beautiful song of Ménétries's Warbler *S mystacea* while at the bottom of a steep rocky wadi in Turkey.

Ménétries's Warbler *Sylvia mystacea* Birecik, Sanlıurfa, Turkey, 19 May 2001. A male singing from the top of a precarious cliff at the side of a narrow wadi. The recording was made from the floor of the wadi. Background: wing-whirr of See-see Partridge *Ammoperdix griseogularis* (0:10), Common Kestrel *Falco tinnunculus*, Greater Short-toed Lark *Calandrella brachydactyla*, Crested Lark *Galerida cristata* and House Sparrow *Passer domesticus*. 01.021.MR.03749.30

CD2-99

As I reach the end of the book my hope is that it will help popularise bird sound identification. During one of the long sessions of work together, Magnus asked me to define what I meant by popularise. "I would like to be able to talk to someone other than you about it, Magnus."

References

American Ornithologists' Union 1998. Checklist of North American birds. Seventh edition. Washington DC.

Arnaiz-Villena, A, Guillén, J, Ruiz-del-Valle, V, Lowy, E, Zamora, J, Varela, P, Stefani, D & Allende, L M 2001. Phylogeography of crossbills, bullfinches, grossbeaks and rosefinches. Cellular and Molecular Life Sciences 58: 1159-1166.

Baptista, L F & Kroodsma, D E 2001. Avian Bioacoustics. In: del Hoyo, J, Elliott, A & Sargatal, J (eds) Handbook of the birds of the world 6. Barcelona.

Becker, P H 1982. The coding of species-specific characteristics in bird sounds. In: Kroodsma, D E & Miller, E H (eds) Acoustic communication in birds 1. New York.

Beletsky, L D 1996. The red-winged blackbird: the biology of a strongly polygynous songbird. San Diego.

Benkman, C W 1992. White-winged Crossbill. In: Poole, A, Stettenheim, P, & Gill, F (eds) The birds of North America 27. Philadelphia/Washington DC.

Benkman, C W 2003. Divergent selection drives the adaptive radiation of crossbills. Evolution 57: 1176-1181.

Bensch, S, Helbig, A J, Salomon, M & Seibold, I 2002. Amplified fragment length polymorphism analysis identifies hybrids between two subspecies of warblers. Molecular Ecology 11: 473-481.

Benson, S V 1952. The observer's book of birds. London.

van den Berg, A B 2006. Dutch Birding's names: list of Western Palarctic bird species 2006. Amsterdam.

van den Berg, A B & Bosman, C A W 2001. Zeldzame vogels van Nederland – Rare birds of the Netherlands. Avifauna van Nederland 1. Second edition. Haarlem.

van den Berg, A B & The Sound Approach 2005. Field identification of Maghreb chaffinches. Dutch Birding 27: 295-301.

Bergmann, H-H & Helb, H-W 1982. Stimmen der Vögel Europas. München.

Birdlife Finland 2001. Lintumme Laulavat – kesän lintuja. Audio CD.

Boon, L J R, Ebels, E B & Robb, M S 2006. Hispaniolan Crossbill. Dutch Birding 28: 99-105.

Bruun, B, Delin, H & Svensson, L 1992. Birds of Britain and Europe ('Hamlyn guide'). London.

Catchpole, C K 1983. Variation in the song of the great reed warbler *Acrocephalus arundinaceus* in relation to mate attraction and territorial defence. Animal Behaviour 31: 1217-1225.

Catchpole, C K & Slater, P J B 1995. Bird song - biological themes and variations. Cambridge, UK.

Chappuis, C 2000. African bird sounds 1. 4 CDs and booklet. Paris.

Confer, J L 1992. Golden-winged Warbler. In: Poole, A , Stettenheim, P & Gills, F (eds) The birds of North America 20. Philadelphia/Washington DC.

Constantine, M 1994. The challenge of bird sounds. Birding World 7: 248-255.

Cramp, S (ed) 1985, 1988, 1992. The birds of the Western Palearctic 4, 5, 6. Oxford.

Cramp, S & Simmons, K E L (eds) 1977, 1980, 1983. The birds of the Western Palearctic 1, 2, 3. Oxford.

Cramp, S & Perrins, C M (eds) 1993, 1994, 1995. The birds of the Western Palearctic 7, 8, 9. Oxford.

Dabelsteen, T & McGregor, P K 1996. Dynamic acoustic communication and interactive playback. In: Kroodsma, D E & Miller, E H (eds) Ecology and evolution of acoustic communication in birds. Ithaca.

Darwin, C 1859. The origin of species by means of natural selection or the preservation of favoured races in the struggle for life. London.

DETR 2001. Achieving a better quality of life: review of progress towards sustainable development. Government annual report 2000. Department of the Environment, Transport and Regions. London.

Dooling, R J 1982. Auditory perception in birds. In: Kroodsma, D E & Miller, E H (eds) Acoustic communication in birds 1. New York.

Dowsett-Lemaire, F 1979. The imitative range of the song of the Marsh Warbler *Acrocephalus palustris*, with special reference to imitations of African birds. Ibis 121: 453-468.

Edelaar, P, Summers, R & Iovchenko, N 2003. The ecology and evolution of crossbills *Loxia* spp: the need for a fresh look and an international research programme. Avian Science 3: 85-93.

Edelaar, P, Robb, M, van Eerde, K, Terpstra, K, Bijlsma, R & Maassen, E 2004. Zijn er meerdere soorten 'gewone' kruisbek in Nederland? Limosa 77: 31-38.

Edwards, P & Watson, R 1986. Song birds. London.

Elliott, L, Stokes, D & Stokes, L 1997. Stokes field guide to bird song: eastern region. Ithaca. 3 CDs and booklet.

Goethe, V F 1937. Beobachtungen und Untersuchungen zur Biologie der Silbermöwe *(Larus a. argentatus)* auf der Vogelinsel Memmertsand. Journal für Ornithologie 85: 1-119.

Goethe, V F 1955. Beobachtungen bei der Aufzucht junger Silbermöwen. Zeitschrift für Tierpsychologie 12: 402-33.

Guyomarc'h, J C, Hemon, Y A, Guyomarc'h, C & Michel, R 1984. La mode de dispersion des mâles de caille des blés, *Coturnix c. coturnix*, en phase de réproduction. Comptes Rendus de l'Académie des Sciences, Paris. Série III 299 (19): 805 808.

Haavie, J, Borge, T, Bures, S, Garamszegi, L Z, Lampe, H M, Moreno, J, Qvarnström, A, Török, J & Sætre, G-P 2004. Flycatcher song in allopatry and sympatry - convergence, divergence and reinforcement. Journal of Evolutionary Biology 17: 227-237.

Hailman, J P & Ficken, M S 1996. Comparative analysis of vocal repertoires, with reference to chickadees. In: Kroodsma, D E & Miller, E H (eds) Ecology and evolution of acoustic communication in birds. Ithaca.

Hallikainen, L 2001. Lunto soi – nature resounds 4. CD.

Heinrich, B 2000. Mind of the raven. Investigations and adventures with wolf-birds. New York.

James, P C 1984. Sexual dimorphism in the voice of the British Storm-petrel, *Hydrobates pelagicus*. Ibis 126: 89-92.

James, P C & Robertson, H A 1985. The calls of male and female Madeiran Storm-Petrels *(Oceanodroma castro)*. Auk 102: 391-393.

Jellis, R 1977. Bird sounds and their meaning. London.

Jonsson, L 1992. Birds of Europe, with North Africa and the Middle East. London.

Kaiser, E 1997. Sexual recognition of Common Swifts. British Birds 90: 167-174.

Kettle, R 1992. British bird sounds on CD. London.

Koch, L 1956. Memoirs of a birdman. London.

Koch, L (ed) 1957. The encyclopedia of British birds. London.

Kroodsma, D E 1982. Learning and the ontogeny of sound signals in birds. In: Kroodsma, D E & Miller, E H (eds). Acoustic communication in birds 2. New York.

Kroodsma, D E 2005. The singing life of birds. New York.

Kroodsma, D E & Miller, E H (eds) 1982. Acoustic communication in birds 1 & 2. New York.

Kroodsma, D E & Miller, E H (eds) 1996. Ecology and evolution of acoustic communication in birds. Ithaca.

Kroodsma, D E, Vielliard, J M E & Stiles, G S 1996. Study of bird sounds in the Neotropics: urgency and opportunity. In: Kroodsma, D E & Miller, E H (eds) Ecology and evolution of acoustic communication in birds. Ithaca.

Lille, R 1988. Art- und Mischgesang von Nachtigall und Sprosser *(Luscinia megarhynchos, L luscinia)*. Journal für Ornithologie 129: 133-159.

Lindholm, A & Aalto, T 2005. The calls of Sykes's and Booted Warblers. Birding World 18: 395-396.

Mammen, D L & Nowicki, S 1981. Individual differences and within-flock convergence in chickadee calls. Behavioral Ecology and Sociobiology 9: 179-186.

Marler, P 1959. Developments in the study of animal communication. In: Bell, P R (ed) Darwin's biological work: some aspects reconsidered. Cambridge.

Marler, P & Slabbekoorn H (eds) 2004. Nature's music - the science of birdsong. New York.

Marshall, H D & Baker, A J 1999. Colonization history of Atlantic Island Chaffinches *(Fringilla coelebs)* revealed by mitochondrial DNA. Molecular Phylogenetics and Evolution 11: 201-212.

McGregor, P K & Dabelsteen, T 1996. Communication networks. In: Kroodsma, D E & Miller, E H (eds) Ecology and evolution of acoustic communication in birds. Ithaca.

Moreno, J M 2000. Cantos y reclamos de las aves de Canarias. 2 CDs and book. Santa Cruz de Tenerife.

Morton, E S 1982. Grading, discreteness, redundancy, and motivation-structural rules. In: Kroodsma, D E & Miller, E H (eds). Acoustic communication in birds 1. New York.

Morton, E S 1996. A comparison of vocal behavior among tropical and temperate passerine birds. In: Kroodsma, D E & Miller, E H (eds) Ecology and evolution of acoustic communication in birds. Ithaca.

Moss, R. & Lockie, I. 1979. Infrasonic components in the song of the Capercaillie *Tetrao urogallus*. Ibis 121: 95-97.

Mullarney, K, Svensson, L, Zetterström, D & Grant, P J 1999. Collins bird guide. London.

Nice, M M 1943. Studies in the life history of the Song Sparrow. Transactions of the Linnean Society New York 6: 1-328.

Nicholson, E M & Koch, L 1936. Songs of wild birds. London.

Oddie, B 1997. Gripping yarns: splinter group. Birdwatch 58: 9.

Parchman, T L, Benkman, C W and Britch, S C 2006. Patterns of genetic variation in the adaptive radiation of New World crossbills (Aves: *Loxia*). Molecular Ecology 15: 1873-1887.

Parkin, D T, Collinson, M, Helbig, A J, Knox, A G, Sangster, G & Svensson, L 2004. Species limits in *Acrocephalus* and *Hippolais* warblers from the Western Palearctic. British Birds 97: 276-299.

Pennington, M G & Meek, E R 2006. The Northern Bullfinch invasion of autumn 2004. British Birds 99: 2-24.

Peterson, R T 1980. A field guide to the birds east of the Rockies. Boston.

Piertney, S, Summers, R W & Marquiss, M 2001. Microsatellite and mitochondrial DNA homogeneity among phenotypically diverse crossbill taxa in the UK. Proceedings of the Royal Society 268: 1511-1517.

Ristow, D & Wink, M 1979. Sexual dimorphism of Cory's Shearwater. Il Merill 21: 9-12.

Robb, M S 2000. Introduction to vocalizations of crossbills in north-western Europe. Dutch Birding 22: 61-107.

Robbins, C S, Bruun, B, Zim, H S & Singer, A 1983. Birds of North America ('Golden field guide'). Revised edition. New York.

Rogers, M 1978. Call-notes of Firecrest and Goldcrest. British Birds 71: 318.

Sample, G 1996. Bird songs & calls of Britain & northern Europe. London.

Sangster, G 1996. How many species of crossbill are there? Dutch Birding 18: 29-32.

Sangster, G 1999. Cryptic species of storm-petrels in the Azores? Dutch Birding 21: 101-106.

Sangster, G, Hazevoet, C J, van den Berg, A B & Roselaar, C S 1998. Dutch avifaunal list: species concepts, taxonomic instability, and taxonomic changes in 1998. Dutch Birding 20: 22-32.

Scott, G W 1999. Separation of Marsh Tits *Parus palustris* and Willow Tits *Parus montanus*. Ringing & Migration 19: 323-327.

Secondi, J, Bretagnole, V, Compagnon, C & Faivre, B 2003. Species-specific song convergence in a moving hybrid zone between two passerines. Biological Journal of the Linnean Society 80: 507-517.

Sibley, D 2000. The North American bird guide. New York.

Smith, P W 1997. The history and taxonomic status of the Hispaniolan Crossbill *Loxia megaplaga*. Bulletin of the British Ornithologists' Club 117: 264-271.

Smith, W J 1996. Using interactive playback to study how songs and singing contribute to communication about behavior. In: Kroodsma, D E & Miller, E H (eds) Ecology and evolution of acoustic communication in birds. Ithaca.

Salomon, M & Hemim, Y 1992. Song variation in the Chiffchaffs *(Phylloscopus collybita)* of the Western Pyrenees – the contact zone between the *collybita* and *brehmii* forms. Ethology 92: 265-282.

Staicer, C A, Spector, D A & Horn, A G 1996. The dawn chorus and other diel patterns in acoustic signalling. In: Kroodsma, D E & Miller, E H (eds) Ecology and evolution of acoustic communication in birds. Ithaca.

Summers, R W, Jardine, D C, Marquiss, M & Rae, R 2002. The distribution and habitats of crossbills *Loxia* spp. in Britain, with special reference to the Scottish Crossbill *Loxia scotica*. Ibis 144: 393-410.

Svensson, L 2001. Identification of Western and Eastern Olivaceous, Booted and Sykes's Warblers. Birding World 14: 192-219.

Templeton, C N, Greene, E & Davis, K 2005. Allometry of alarm calls: Black-capped Chickadees encode information about predator size. Science 308: 1934-1937.

Thielcke, G 1969. Geographic variation in bird vocalizations. In: Hinde, R A (ed) Bird vocalizations: 311-339. London/New York.

Thielcke, G A 1976. Bird sounds. Ann Arbor.

Thorpe, W H 1961. Bird-song. Cambridge monographs in experimental biology 12. Cambridge.

Tschanz, B 1968. Trottellummen. Zeitschrift für Tierpsychologie 4: 1-103.

Vince, M A 1969. Embryonic communication, respiration and the synchronisation of hatching. In: Hinde, R A (ed) Bird vocalizations – their relation to current problems in biology and psychology. Cambridge.

Weiner, J 1995. The beak of the finch. New York.

West, M J, Stroud, A N & King, A P 1983. Mimicry of the human voice by European Starlings: the role of social interaction. Wilson Bulletin 95: 635-640.

West, M & King, A 1996. A systems approach to the ontogeny of avian communication. In: Kroodsma, D E & Miller, E H (eds) Ecology and evolution of acoustic communication in birds. Ithaca.

Zink, R M 2002. A new perspective on the evolutionary history of Darwin's finches. Auk 119: 864-871.

Index